What is the purpose of the I ♥ READING BOOKS?

This set of 190 books utilizes highly decodable text to provide children with independent blending and reading practice. Two four-page books (a Book and a Review Book) focus on *each* phonic and key structural analysis element taught in **Houghton Mifflin Reading.** For example, two books are provided for the *a_e, ai,* and *ay* spellings of long *a,* as well as for the /d/, /t/, and /ĕd/ pronunciations for the ending *-ed.*

Since many of the words in each book contain the target skill, children gain the specific practice they need to build fluency. For reference, each book includes a list to show all the words (decodable and high-frequency) and skills featured in it.

To give children practice reading in different genres, **I Love Reading Books** include both fiction and nonfiction selections.

How are the I ♥ READING BOOKS organized?

The **I Love Reading Books** are divided into themes that correlate with instruction in **Houghton Mifflin Reading.** Levels 1.1 - 1.2 are bound in the first volume, and Levels 1.3 - 1.5 are in the second. One book per skill appears in the first half of each volume, numbered consecutively. Flip the volume over to find the review books, also numbered consecutively.

When do I use I ♥ READING BOOKS?

• Users of **Houghton Mifflin Reading** will find references to the **I Love Reading Books** in the **Teacher's Edition** following the Phonics, Phonics Review, and Phonics Reteaching lessons.

• You can use the books as application after introducing a new sound/spelling with **Houghton Mifflin Sound/Spelling Cards.**
• The books are also an excellent resource any time a child needs extra practice reading words with a specific sound/spelling.

How can I use I ♥ READING BOOKS to meet my specific classroom needs?

• Help children to differentiate between two or more similar sound/spellings by reading and comparing books that feature them.
• Have English language learners focus on sounds and spellings they find difficult in English by reading books aloud to one another.
• Informally assess children's understanding of a new skill by having them read a book aloud to you.

What is the easiest way to set up I ♥ READING BOOKS in my classroom?

Every classroom is different. You may choose to provide children with the books only as they need them, or you may set up a classroom area where children may take and use **I Love Reading Books** on their own throughout the school year. Consider these options:

• Keep copies of books on file for children to take home or read and color in the classroom.
• Keep a laminated set of books for children to read in class.
• Set up a chart for children to track their own progress as they read each book independently.

This chart shows which **I love READING BOOKS** correspond to the **Houghton Mifflin Sound/Spelling Cards.**

Book & Review Book	Skill	Sound/ Spelling Cards
1	m, s, c, t, short a	Apple, Cat, Mouse, Seal, Tiger
2	consonant n	Noodle
3	consonant f	Fish
4	consonant p	Pig
5	short i	Iguana
6	consonant b	Bear
7	consonant r	Rooster
8	consonant h	Horse
9	consonant g	Goose
10	short o	Ostrich
11	consonant d	Duck
12	consonant w	Worm
13	consonant l	Lion
14	consonant x	Fox
15	short e	Elephant
16	consonant y	Yo-yo
17	consonant k	Cat
18	consonant v	Volcano
19	short u	Umbrella
20	/kw/ spelled qu	Queen
21	consonant j	Jumping Jill
22	consonant z	Zebra
23	/z/ spelled s	Zebra
24	consonants -ck	Cat
27	/s/ spelled -ss	Seal
28	/t/ spelled -ed	Tiger
29	/d/ spelled -ed	Duck
34	silent k in kn	Noodle
35	silent w in wr	Rooster
36	silent g in gn	Noodle
38	digraph sh	Sheep
39	digraph th	Thumb
40	digraph wh	Whale
41	digraph ch	Chick
42	digraph -tch	Chick
43	long a (CVCe)	Acorn

Book & Review Book	Skill	Sound/ Spelling Cards
44	/s/ spelled c	Seal
45	/j/ spelled g	Jumping Jill
49	long i (CVCe)	Ice Cream
51	long o (CV)	Ocean
52	long o (CVCe)	Ocean
54	/yōō/ spelled u (CVCe)	Unicorn
58	long e (CV)	Eagle
59	long e (CVCe)	Eagle
60	long e spelled ee	Eagle
61	long e spelled ea	Eagle
62	long a spelled ai	Acorn
63	long a spelled ay	Acorn
64	long o spelled oa	Ocean
65	long o spelled ow	Ocean
66	/ōō/ spelled oo	Cook
67	/ōō/ spelled oo	Moon
68	/ōō/ spelled ew	Moon
69	/ōō/ spelled ue	Moon
70	/ōō/ spelled ou	Moon
71	long i spelled igh	Ice Cream
72	long i spelled ie	Ice Cream
76	/ou/ spelled ou	Owl
77	/ou/ spelled ow	Owl
80	long e spelled y	Eagle
81	long i spelled y	Ice Cream
84	/oi/ spelled oi	Boy
85	/oi/ spelled oy	Boy
86	/ô/ spelled aw	Saw
87	/ô/ spelled au	Saw
88	r-controlled or	Orange
89	r-controlled ore	Orange
90	r-controlled er	Bird
91	r-controlled ir	Bird
92	r-controlled ur	Bird
93	r-controlled ar	Artist

I ♥ (LOVE) READING BOOKS

THEME 1
All Together Now

BOOK 1	Sam Sat, Cat Sat
BOOK 2	Nan Can Nap
BOOK 3	Fan Fan Fan
BOOK 4	Tap, Tap, Tap
BOOK 5	Big, Big Fig

BOOK 6	Here, Bam Bam
BOOK 7	Rap! Rap! Rap!
BOOK 8	Ham! Ham! Ham!
BOOK 9	Big, Big Rig

Sam Sat, Cat Sat

Sam Sat, Cat Sat

HOUGHTON MIFFLIN   BOSTON

HIGH-FREQUENCY WORDS TAUGHT TO DATE

Grade 1

(No high-frequency words have been taught to date.)

Sam sat.

Sam Sat, Cat Sat

Sam sat. Cat sat.

Cat!

2

Cat sat.

3

Nan Can Nap

DECODABLE WORDS

Target Skill: consonant *n*

can	nap
Nan	pan

Previously Taught Skills

(Words listed under *Target Skill* also include previously taught skills.)

SKILLS APPLIED IN WORDS IN STORY: *m, s, c, t,* short *a;* consonant *p*

HIGH–FREQUENCY WORDS

on

the

Nan Can Nap

HIGH-FREQUENCY WORDS TAUGHT TO DATE

Grade 1

go
on
the

Decoding skills taught to date: *m, s, c, t,* short *a;* consonant *n;* consonant *f;* consonant *p*

Nan Can Nap

Nan can nap.

Nan can nap.

Nap, nap, nap.

Can Nan nap on the can?

2

Can Nan nap on the pan?

Fan Fan Fan

DECODABLE WORDS

Target Skill: consonant *f*

fan

Previously Taught Skills

can	Pam
cat	Sam

SKILLS APPLIED IN WORDS IN STORY: *m, s, c, t,* short *a*; consonant *n*; consonant *p*

HIGH–FREQUENCY WORDS

the

HOUGHTON MIFFLIN   BOSTON

Fan Fan Fan

HIGH-FREQUENCY WORDS TAUGHT TO DATE

Grade 1

go
on
the

Decoding skills taught to date: m, s, c, t, short a; consonant n; consonant f; consonant p

Fan Fan Fan

The cat can fan Sam.

Pam can fan Sam.

Fan, fan, fan.

Sam can fan.

Fan, fan, fan.

4

1

Fan the cat, Sam.

Fan Pam, Sam.

2

3

Tap, Tap, Tap

DECODABLE WORDS

Target Skill: consonant *p*

Pam   tap
Pat

Previously Taught Skills

can

SKILLS APPLIED IN WORDS IN STORY: *m, s, c, t,* short *a;* consonant *n*

HIGH–FREQUENCY WORDS

go

HOUGHTON MIFFLIN   BOSTON

Tap, Tap, Tap

HIGH-FREQUENCY WORDS TAUGHT TO DATE

Grade 1

go
on
the

Decoding skills taught to date: *m, s, c, t,* short *a;* consonant *n;* consonant *f;* consonant *p*

Tap, Tap, Tap

Pam   Pat

Go, Pam!

Go, Pat!

Tap, tap, tap!

4

1

Pam can tap.

Pat can tap.

Big, Big Fig

DECODABLE WORDS

Target Skill: short *i*

big	bit	in	Mim
bin	fig	is	

Previously Taught Skills

(Words listed under *Target Skill* also include previously taught skills.)

SKILLS APPLIED IN WORDS IN STORY: *m, s, c, t,* short *a*; consonant *n*; consonant *f*; consonant *b*; consonant *g*

HIGH–FREQUENCY WORDS

here

the

HOUGHTON MIFFLIN   BOSTON

Big, Big Fig

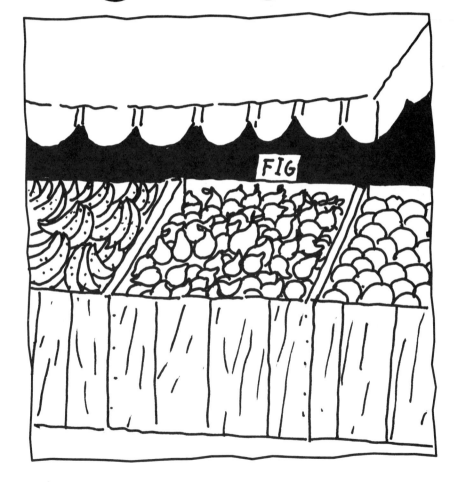

HIGH-FREQUENCY WORDS TAUGHT TO DATE

Grade 1

and
go
here
jump
not
on
the
too
we

Decoding skills taught to date: *m, s, c, t,* short *a;* consonant *n;* consonant *f;* consonant *p;* short *i;* consonant *b;* consonant *r;* consonant *h;* consonant *g*

Mim bit the big, big fig.

4

Big, Big Fig

Here is Mim.

Here is the fig bin.

The big fig is in the bin.

The fig is big. Big, big fig!

Here, Bam Bam!

Target Skill: consonant *b*

bag	bib
Bam	bit

Previously Taught Skills

sat

sit

SKILLS APPLIED IN WORDS IN STORY: *m, s, c, t,* short *a*; short *i*; consonant *g*

here

the

HOUGHTON MIFFLIN   BOSTON

Copyright©Houghton Mifflin Company. All rights reserved.

Here, Bam Bam!

HIGH-FREQUENCY WORDS TAUGHT TO DATE

Grade 1

and
go
here
jump
not
on
the
too
we

Decoding skills taught to date: *m, s, c, t,* short *a;* consonant *n;* consonant *f;* consonant *p;* short *i;* consonant *b;* consonant *r;* consonant *h;* consonant *g*

Here, Bam Bam!

Bam Bam sat.

Bam Bam bit the bag.

Bam Bam bit the bib.

Sit, Bam Bam!

Rap! Rap! Rap!

DECODABLE WORDS

Target Skill: consonant *r*

ran   rig
rap   rip

Previously Taught Skills

big   is   Nan
can   it   sit

SKILLS APPLIED IN WORDS IN STORY: *m, s, c, t,* short *a;* consonant *n;* consonant *p;* short *i;* consonant *b;* consonant *g*

HIGH–FREQUENCY WORDS

go   the
here   we

HOUGHTON MIFFLIN   BOSTON

Rap! Rap! Rap!

HIGH-FREQUENCY WORDS TAUGHT TO DATE

Grade 1

and
go
here
jump
not
on
the
too
we

Decoding skills taught to date: *m, s, c, t,* short *a;* consonant *n;* consonant *f;* consonant *p;* short *i;* consonant *b;* consonant *r;* consonant *h;* consonant *g*

Sit here, Nan.

The rig can go!

4

Rap! Rap! Rap!

Rap, rap, rap!

Is it Nan?

1

We ran, ran, ran.

It is Nan!

2

Rip, rip, rip!
Here is the big rig!

3

Ham! Ham! Ham!

DECODABLE WORDS

Target Skill: consonant *h*

ham
has

Previously Taught Skills

is   Tim

Mim

SKILLS APPLIED IN WORDS IN STORY: *m, s, c, t,* short *a;* short *i*

HIGH–FREQUENCY WORDS

here
the

HOUGHTON MIFFLIN   BOSTON

Ham! Ham! Ham!

HIGH-FREQUENCY WORDS TAUGHT TO DATE

Grade 1

and
go
here
jump
not
on
the
too
we

Decoding skills taught to date: *m, s, c, t,* short *a;* consonant *n;* consonant *f;* consonant *p;* short *i;* consonant *b;* consonant *r;* consonant *h;* consonant *g*

Copyright © Houghton Mifflin Company. All rights reserved.

Ham! Ham! Ham!

Ham! Ham! Ham!

4

Here is the ham!
Ham! Ham! Ham!

1

Tim has ham!

Mim has ham!

Big, Big Rig

DECODABLE WORDS

Target Skill: consonant *g*

big
rig

Previously Taught Skills

in	it
is	sit

SKILLS APPLIED IN WORDS IN STORY: *m, s, c, t,* short *a;* consonant *n;* short *i;* consonant *b;* consonant *r*

HIGH–FREQUENCY WORDS

go
the
we

Big, Big Rig

HOUGHTON MIFFLIN   BOSTON

HIGH-FREQUENCY WORDS TAUGHT TO DATE

Grade 1
and
go
here
jump
not
on
the
too
we

Decoding skills taught to date: m, s, c, t, short a; consonant n; consonant f; consonant p; short i; consonant b; consonant r; consonant h; consonant g

Go, big, big rig!

Big, Big Rig

It is the big, big rig!
It is big, big, big!

We go in the big, big rig.

We sit in the big, big rig.

I ♥ READING BOOKS

THEME 2
Surprise!

BOOK 10   The Fox and Dog
BOOK 11   Dig and Dip
BOOK 12   Wag, Wag, Win!
BOOK 13   Lin Has a Lab
BOOK 14   Max Can Mix
BOOK 15   At the Vet
BOOK 16   Yak

BOOK 17   Kim and Kip
BOOK 18   Viv and Vic
BOOK 19   Yum! Yum!
BOOK 20   Quig Pig!
BOOK 21   Jim and Jan Jig
BOOK 22   The Big Zig-Zag

The Fox and Dog

DECODABLE WORDS

Target Skill: short *o*

Dog	hop	Mom	Ron
fox	log	Pop	

Previously Taught Skills

can

SKILLS APPLIED IN WORDS IN STORY: *m, s, c, t,* short *a;* consonant *n;* consonant *f;* consonant *p;* consonant *r;* consonant *h;* consonant *g;* consonant *d;* consonant *l;* consonant *x*

HIGH–FREQUENCY WORDS

a	on
and	the
find	

short o

BOOK 10

The Fox and Dog

HIGH-FREQUENCY WORDS TAUGHT TO DATE

Grade 1

a
and
find
go
have
here
jump
not
on
one
the
to
too
we
who

Decoding skills taught to date: m, s, c, t, short *a;* consonant *n;* consonant *f;* consonant *p;* short *i;* consonant *b;* consonant *r;* consonant *h;* consonant *g;* short *o;* consonant *d;* consonant *w;* consonant *l;* consonant *x*

Can Dog find the fox?

Fox? Fox? Fox?

4

The Fox and Dog

Mom and Pop

Ron and Dog

1

A fox on a log!

Ron and Dog hop on a log.

Dig and Dip

DECODABLE WORDS

Target Skill: consonant *d*

Dad	Don	dip
Dog	dig	

Previously Taught Skills

can	Mom
hop	mop

SKILLS APPLIED IN WORDS IN STORY: *m, s, c, t,* short *a*; consonant *n*; consonant *p*; short *i*; consonant *h*; consonant *g*; short *o*

HIGH-FREQUENCY WORDS

and
find
the

HOUGHTON MIFFLIN   BOSTON

Dig and Dip

HIGH-FREQUENCY WORDS TAUGHT TO DATE

Grade 1

a
and
find
go
have
here
jump
not
on
one
the
to
too
we
who

Decoding skills taught to date: *m, s, c, t,* short *a;* consonant *n;* consonant *f;* consonant *p;* short *i;* consonant *b;* consonant *r;* consonant *h;* consonant *g;* short *o;* consonant *d;* consonant *w;* consonant *l;* consonant *x*

Don Dog can dip the mop.

Dip the mop, Don.

Dip, dip!

4

Dig and Dip

Don Dog can dig.

Dig, dig, dig, Don!

1

Don Dog can hop.
Hop, hop, Don!

Can Dad and Mom
find Don Dog?

2

3

Wag, Wag, Win!

DECODABLE WORDS

Target Skill: consonant w

wag

win

Previously Taught Skills

big	hit	it
got	is	tap

SKILLS APPLIED IN WORDS IN STORY: *m, s, c, t,* short *a*; consonant *n*; consonant *p*; short *i*; consonant *b*; consonant *h*; consonant *g*; short *o*

HIGH-FREQUENCY WORDS

a

we

HOUGHTON MIFFLIN   BOSTON

Wag, Wag, Win!

HIGH-FREQUENCY WORDS TAUGHT TO DATE

Grade 1

a
and
find
go
have
here
jump
not
on
one
the
to
too
we
who

Decoding skills taught to date: m, s, c, t, short a; consonant n; consonant f; consonant p; short i; consonant b; consonant r; consonant h; consonant g; short o; consonant d; consonant w; consonant l; consonant x

Wag, Wag, Win!

We wag, wag, wag.

We win! We win!

Wag, wag, wag.

We tap, tap, tap.

2

We got a hit!
It is a big, big, big hit!

3

Lin Has a Lab

DECODABLE WORDS

Target Skill: consonant _l_

lab	lit
Lin	

Previously Taught Skills

gas	hot
has	mix

SKILLS APPLIED IN WORDS IN STORY: _m, s, c, t,_ short _a;_ consonant _n;_ short _i;_ consonant _b;_ consonant _h;_ consonant _g;_ short _o;_ consonant _x_

HIGH-FREQUENCY WORDS

a

the

HOUGHTON MIFFLIN   BOSTON

Lin Has a Lab

Grade 1

a
and
find
go
have
here
jump
not
on
one
the
to
too
we
who

Decoding skills taught to date: *m, s, c, t,* short *a;* consonant *n;* consonant *f;* consonant *p;* short *i;* consonant *b;* consonant *r;* consonant *h;* consonant *g;* short *o;* consonant *d;* consonant *w;* consonant *l;* consonant *x*

Lin Has a Lab

Lin has a lab.

Lin has a hot mix!

4

Lin has a mix.

Lin lit the gas.

Max Can Mix

DECODABLE WORDS

Target Skill: consonant *x*

box   Max
fix   mix

Previously Taught Skills

can   it
has   Mom

SKILLS APPLIED IN WORDS IN STORY: *m, s, c, t,* short *a*; consonant *n*; consonant *f*; short *i*; consonant *b*; consonant *h*; short *o*

HIGH–FREQUENCY WORDS

a

HOUGHTON MIFFLIN   BOSTON

Max Can Mix

HIGH-FREQUENCY WORDS TAUGHT TO DATE

Grade 1

a
and
find
go
have
here
jump
not
on
one
the
to
too
we
who

Decoding skills taught to date: *m, s, c, t,* short *a;* consonant *n;* consonant *f;* consonant *p;* short *i;* consonant *b;* consonant *r;* consonant *h;* consonant *g;* short *o;* consonant *d;* consonant *w;* consonant *l;* consonant *x*

Max Can Mix

Mom has a box.

Fix, Max. Fix!

4

1

Max can mix.
Mix, Max. Mix!

2

Can Max fix it?

3

At the Vet

DECODABLE WORDS

Target Skill: short *e*

bed	Ed	led	wet
beg	fed	leg	yet
Ben	get	vet	

Previously Taught Skills

at	Dad	his
bad	Dog	nap
can	had	

SKILLS APPLIED IN WORDS IN STORY: *m, s, c, t,* short *a*; consonant *n*; consonant *f*; consonant *p*; short *i*; consonant *b*; consonant *h*; consonant *g*; short *o*; consonant *d*; consonant *w*; consonant *l*; consonant *y*; consonant *v*

HIGH–FREQUENCY WORDS

a	jump	the
and	not	to
in		

HOUGHTON MIFFLIN   BOSTON

short *e*
BOOK 15

At the Vet

HIGH-FREQUENCY WORDS TAUGHT TO DATE

Grade 1

a
and
find
five
four
go
have
here
in
jump
not
on
once
one
the
three
to
too
two
upon
we
what
who

Decoding skills taught to date: m, s, c, t, short a; consonant n; consonant f; consonant p; short i; consonant b; consonant r; consonant h; consonant g; short o; consonant d; consonant w; consonant l; consonant x; short e; consonant y; consonant k; consonant v

Ed Dog can not jump yet.

Ed Dog **can** beg.

Beg, Ed Dog! Beg!

4

At the Vet

Ed Dog had a bad leg.

Ben and Dad led Ed Dog

to the vet.

1

Ed Dog can not jump yet.

His leg can not get wet.

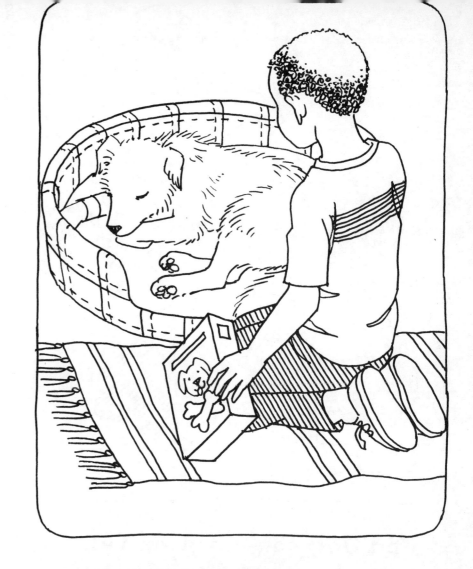

Ben fed Ed Dog.

Ed Dog had a nap in bed.

Yak

DECODABLE WORDS

Target Skill: consonant y

Yak	Yan	yet
yam	yes	

Previously Taught Skills

can	has	it
fed	is	sad

SKILLS APPLIED IN WORDS IN STORY: *m, s, c, t,* short *a;* consonant *n;* consonant *f;* short *i;* consonant *h;* short *o;* consonant *d;* short *e;* consonant *k*

HIGH–FREQUENCY WORDS

a	the
have	
not	

HOUGHTON MIFFLIN   BOSTON

Yak

HIGH-FREQUENCY WORDS TAUGHT TO DATE

Grade 1

a
and
find
five
four
go
have
here
in
jump
not
on
once
one
the
three
to
too
two
upon
we
what
who

Decoding skills taught to date: m, s, c, t, short *a;* consonant *n;* consonant *f;* consonant *p;* short *i;* consonant *b;* consonant *r;* consonant *h;* consonant *g;* short *o;* consonant *d;* consonant *w;* consonant *l;* consonant *x;* short *e;* consonant *y;* consonant *k;* consonant *v*

Yan fed Yak the yam.

4

Yak

Yan has a yam. Can Yak have it?

1

Yak can not have the yam yet.
Yak is sad, sad, sad.

2

Can Yak have the yam yet?
Yes, Yes, Yes!
Yak can have the yam.
Yak is not sad!

3

Kim and Kip

DECODABLE WORDS

Target Skill: consonant *k*

Kim   Kit

Kip

Previously Taught Skills

can   got   ran

Cat   is

SKILLS APPLIED IN WORDS IN STORY: *m, s, c, t,* short *a*; consonant *n*; consonant *p*;
short *i*; consonant *r*; consonant *g*; short *o*

HIGH–FREQUENCY WORDS

and   here   the

find   not   to

HOUGHTON MIFFLIN   BOSTON

Kim and Kip

Grade 1

a
and
find
five
four
go
have
here
in
jump
not
on
once
one
the
three
to
too
two
upon
we
what
who

Decoding skills taught to date: *m, s, c, t,* short *a;* consonant *n;* consonant *f;* consonant *p;* short *i;* consonant *b;* consonant *r;* consonant *h;* consonant *g;* short *o;* consonant *d;* consonant *w;* consonant *l;* consonant *x;* short *e;* consonant *y;* consonant *k;* consonant *v*

Kim and Kip

Kim can not find Kip Cat.

"Kip! Kip! Kip!"

1

Kip Cat ran to Kim.

"Kip! Kip! Kip!"

4

Is Kip Cat here?

"Kip! Kip! Kip!"

Kip Cat is not here.

Kim got the Kip Cat Kit.

"Here, Kip!"

2

3

Viv and Vic

DECODABLE WORDS

Target Skill: consonant *v*

van	Viv
Vic	Vvvvrrrrr

Previously Taught Skills

big	can	has
box	got	

SKILLS APPLIED IN WORDS IN STORY: *m, s, c, t,* short *a;* consonant *n;* short *i;* consonant *b;* consonant *r;* consonant *h;* consonant *g;* short *o;* consonant *x*

HIGH–FREQUENCY WORDS

a	the
and	too
have	

Viv and Vic

HIGH-FREQUENCY WORDS TAUGHT TO DATE

Grade 1

a
and
find
five
four
go
have
here
in
jump
not
on
once
one
the
three
to
too
two
upon
we
what
who

Decoding skills taught to date: *m, s, c, t,* short *a;* consonant *n;* consonant *f;* consonant *p;* short *i;* consonant *b;* consonant *r;* consonant *h;* consonant *g;* short *o;* consonant *d;* consonant *w;* consonant *l;* consonant *x;* short *e;* consonant *y;* consonant *k;* consonant *v*

Viv and Vic

Vic got a big, big, van!
"Vvvvrrrrr!"

Viv has a big van.
Viv has a big box, too.

Can Vic have the big box?

Vic **can** have the big box!

Yum! Yum!

DECODABLE WORDS

Target Skill: short *u*

bun	cup	jug	run
Cub	cut	mug	yum

Previously Taught Skills

Mom

SKILLS APPLIED IN WORDS IN STORY: *m, s, c, t,* short *a;* consonant *n;* consonant *p;* consonant *b;* consonant *r;* consonant *g;* short *o;* consonant *y;* consonant *j*

HIGH–FREQUENCY WORDS

and

the

HOUGHTON MIFFLIN   BOSTON

Yum! Yum!

HIGH-FREQUENCY WORDS TAUGHT TO DATE

Grade 1

a
and
do
find
five
for
four
go
have
here
I
in
is
jump
me
my
not
on
once
one
said
the
three
to
too
two
upon
we
what
who
you

Decoding skills taught to date: *m, s, c, t,* short *a;* consonant *n;* consonant *f;* consonant *p;* short *i;* consonant *b;* consonant *r;* consonant *h;* consonant *g;* short *o;* consonant *d;* consonant *w;* consonant *l;* consonant *x;* short *e;* consonant *y;* consonant *k;* consonant *v;* short *u;* /kw/ spelled *qu;* consonant *j;* consonant *z*

Yum! Yum! Yum!

4

Yum! Yum!

Mom and Cub run.

1

jug

mug

cup

Mom cut the bun.

2

3

Quig Pig!

DECODABLE WORDS

Target Skill: /kw/ spelled *qu*

Quig
quit

Previously Taught Skills

big	fig	jam	Pig	ten
bun	get	lot	six	up
did	had	nut		

SKILLS APPLIED IN WORDS IN STORY: *m, s, c, t*, short *a*; consonant *n*; consonant *f*; consonant *p*; short *i*; consonant *b*; consonant *h*; consonant *g*; short *o*; consonant *d*; consonant *l*; consonant *x*; short *e*; short *u*; consonant *j*

HIGH-FREQUENCY WORDS

a
and
not

HOUGHTON MIFFLIN   BOSTON

Quig Pig!

Grade 1

a
and
do
find
five
for
four
go
have
here
I
in
is
jump
me
my
not
on
once
one
said
the
three
to
too
two
upon
we
what
who
you

Decoding skills taught to date: *m, s, c, t,* short *a;* consonant *n;* consonant *f;* consonant *p;* short *i;* consonant *b;* consonant *r;* consonant *h;* consonant *g;* short *o;* consonant *d;* consonant *w;* consonant *l;* consonant *x;* short *e;* consonant *y;* consonant *k;* consonant *v;* short *u;* /kw/ spelled *qu;* consonant *j;* consonant *z*

Quig Pig!

Quig had a fig.
Quig had six!

1

Quig did not get up.
Quig quit!

4

Quig had a nut.
Quig had a lot!

Quig had a big bun and jam.
Quig had ten!

2

3

Jim and Jan Jig

DECODABLE WORDS

Target Skill: consonant *j*

jam	jig
Jan	Jim

Previously Taught Skills

get

tap

SKILLS APPLIED IN WORDS IN STORY: *m, s, c, t,* short *a*; consonant *n*; consonant *p*; short *i*; consonant *g*; short *e*

HIGH–FREQUENCY WORDS

and

jump

Jim and Jan Jig

HOUGHTON MIFFLIN   BOSTON

HIGH-FREQUENCY WORDS TAUGHT TO DATE

Grade 1

a
and
do
find
five
for
four
go
have
here
I
in
is
jump
me
my
not
on
once
one
said
the
three
to
too
two
upon
we
what
who
you

Decoding skills taught to date: m, s, c, t, short a; consonant n; consonant f; consonant p; short i; consonant b; consonant r; consonant h; consonant g; short o; consonant d; consonant w; consonant l; consonant x; short e; consonant y; consonant k; consonant v; short u; /kw/ spelled qu; consonant j; consonant z

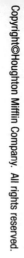

Jim and Jan get jam.

4

Jim and Jan Jig

Jim and Jan jig.

1

Jim and Jan tap.

Jim and Jan jump.

The Big Zig-Zag

DECODABLE WORDS

Target Skill: consonant z

zag   zig

zap   zig-zag

Previously Taught Skills

big

SKILLS APPLIED IN WORDS IN STORY: *m, s, c, t,* short *a*; consonant *p*; short *i*; consonant *b*; consonant *g*

HIGH-FREQUENCY WORDS

I

the

The Big Zig-Zag

HOUGHTON MIFFLIN   BOSTON

HIGH-FREQUENCY WORDS TAUGHT TO DATE

Grade 1

a
and
do
find
five
for
four
go
have
here
I
in
is
jump
me
my
not
on
once
one
said
the
three
to
too
two
upon
we
what
who
you

Decoding skills taught to date: *m, s, c, t,* short *a;* consonant *n;* consonant *f;* consonant *p;* short *i;* consonant *b;* consonant *r;* consonant *h;* consonant *g;* short *o;* consonant *d;* consonant *w;* consonant *l;* consonant *x;* short *e;* consonant *y;* consonant *k;* consonant *v;* short *u;* /kw/ spelled *qu;* consonant *j;* consonant *z*

The Big Zig-Zag

I zig. Zig, zig, zig.

1

Zig, zag, ZAP!

4

I zag. Zag, zag, zag.

2

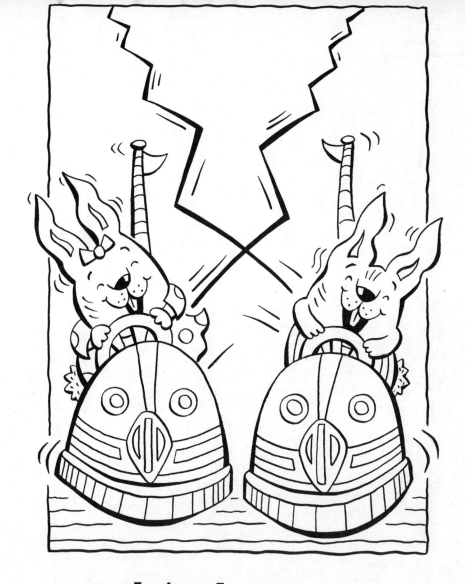

I zig. I zag.
Zig, zag. Zig, zag.

3

I ♥ LOVE READING BOOKS

THEME 3
Let's Look Around!

BOOK 23   Kids, Moms, Dads

BOOK 24   Mack Packs His Sack

BOOK 25   Get Well, Bell Doll!

BOOK 26   Jeff and Ruff

BOOK 27   Can Jess Get a Bass?

BOOK 28   The Ducks Quacked

BOOK 29   Sis Yelled

BOOK 30   Fixing a Van

BOOK 31   Drips and Drops on Gran

Kids, Moms, Dads

DECODABLE WORDS

Target Skill: /z/ spelled *s*

buns	dads	hams	kids	pans
cans	dogs	jugs	moms	yams

Previously Taught Skills

cups	hot	run
fun	pop	

SKILLS APPLIED IN WORDS IN STORY: *m, s, c, t,* short *a*; consonant *n*; consonant *f*; consonant *p*; short *i*; consonant *b*; consonant *r*; consonant *h*; consonant *g*; short *o*; consonant *d*; consonant *y*; consonant *k*; short *u*; consonant *j*

HIGH-FREQUENCY WORDS

and   have

on

HOUGHTON MIFFLIN   BOSTON

Kids, Moms, Dads

HIGH-FREQUENCY WORDS TAUGHT TO DATE

Grade 1

a	two
and	upon
are	we
away	what
do	where
does	who
find	you
five	
for	
four	
go	
have	
he	
here	
I	
in	
is	
jump	
live	
me	
my	
not	
on	
once	
one	
pull	
said	
the	
they	
three	
to	
too	

Decoding skills taught to date: *m, s, c, t,* short *a;* consonant *n;* consonant *f;* consonant *p;* short *i;* consonant *b;* consonant *r;* consonant *h;* consonant *g;* short *o;* consonant *d;* consonant *w;* consonant *l;* consonant *x;* short *e;* consonant *y;* consonant *k;* consonant *v;* short *u;* /kw/ spelled *qu;* consonant *j;* consonant *z;* /z/ spelled *s;* consonants *-ck;* /l/ spelled *-ll;* /f/ spelled *-ff;* /s/ spelled *-ss*

Kids, moms, and dads run.

4

Kids, Moms, Dads

Kids, moms, and dads have fun.

1

Hot dogs on buns!
Hams and yams on pans!

Jugs, cups, and cans!

2

3

Mack Packs His Sack

DECODABLE WORDS

Target Skill: consonants -ck

back	packs	sacks	Zack
Mack	sack	socks	

Previously Taught Skills

bus   his

has

SKILLS APPLIED IN WORDS IN STORY: *m, s, c, t*, short *a*; consonant *n*; consonant *p*; short *i*; consonant *b*; consonant *h*; short *o*; short *u*; consonant *z*; /z/ spelled *s*

HIGH–FREQUENCY WORDS

and	on
go	the
in	too

HOUGHTON MIFFLIN   BOSTON

Mack Packs His Sack

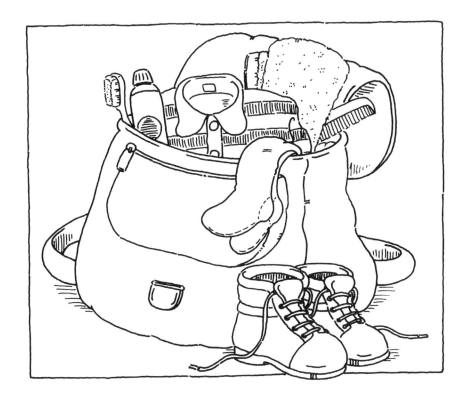

HIGH-FREQUENCY WORDS TAUGHT TO DATE

Grade 1

a	two
and	upon
are	we
away	what
do	where
does	who
find	you
five	
for	
four	
go	
have	
he	
here	
I	
in	
is	
jump	
live	
me	
my	
not	
on	
once	
one	
pull	
said	
the	
they	
three	
to	
too	

Decoding skills taught to date: m, s, c, t, short a; consonant n; consonant f; consonant p; short i; consonant b; consonant r; consonant h; consonant g; short o; consonant d; consonant w; consonant l; consonant x; short e; consonant y; consonant k; consonant v; short u; /kw/ spelled qu; consonant j; consonant z; /z/ spelled s; consonants -ck; /l/ spelled -ll; /f/ spelled -ff; /s/ spelled -ss

Mack Packs His Sack

Mack has his sack on his back.

Zack has his sack on his back.

4

Mack packs socks in his sack.

1

Zack has socks in his sack, too!

Mack and Zack go on the bus.

The sacks go on the bus, too!

Get Well, Bell Doll

DECODABLE WORDS

Target Skill: /l/ spelled -ll

Bell	fell	sill	will
Doll	Lill	well	

Previously Taught Skills

bed	got	tuck
get	set	

SKILLS APPLIED IN WORDS IN STORY: *m, s, c, t,* short *a;* consonant *n;* consonant *f;* short *i;* consonant *b;* consonant *g;* short *o;* consonant *d;* consonant *w;* consonant *l;* short *e;* short *u;* /z/ spelled *s;* consonants *-ck*

HIGH–FREQUENCY WORDS

a	is	the
are	on	you
in	said	

Get Well, Bell Doll!

HOUGHTON MIFFLIN   BOSTON

HIGH-FREQUENCY WORDS TAUGHT TO DATE

Grade 1

a	two
and	upon
are	we
away	what
do	where
does	who
find	you
five	
for	
four	
go	
have	
he	
here	
I	
in	
is	
jump	
live	
me	
my	
not	
on	
once	
one	
pull	
said	
the	
they	
three	
to	
too	

Decoding skills taught to date: m, s, c, t, short a; consonant n; consonant f; consonant p; short i; consonant b; consonant r; consonant h; consonant g; short o; consonant d; consonant w; consonant l; consonant x; short e; consonant y; consonant k; consonant v; short u; /kw/ spelled qu; consonant j; consonant z; /z/ spelled s; consonants -ck; /l/ spelled -ll; /f/ spelled -ff; /s/ spelled -ss

Get Well,
Bell Doll!

Lill got a doll.
The doll is Bell.

1

Lill will tuck Bell Doll in bed.
Bell Doll will get well!

4

Lill set Bell Doll on a sill.
Bell Doll fell.

"You fell Bell Doll," said Lill.
"Are you well?"

2

3

Jeff and Ruff

DECODABLE WORDS

Target Skill: /f/ spelled -ff

huff	puff
Jeff	Ruff

Previously Taught Skills

big	hill	pack	up
dog	his	sit	will
has	lug	top	

SKILLS APPLIED IN WORDS IN STORY: *m, s, c, t,* short *a;* consonant *p;* short *i;* consonant *b;* consonant *r;* consonant *h;* consonant *g;* short *o;* consonant *d;* consonant *w;* consonant *l;* short *e;* short *u;* consonant *j;* /z/ spelled *s;* consonants *-ck;* /l/ spelled *-ll*

HIGH–FREQUENCY WORDS

a	here	to
and	is	too
go	the	

HOUGHTON MIFFLIN   BOSTON

Jeff and Ruff

HIGH-FREQUENCY WORDS TAUGHT TO DATE

Grade 1

a	two
and	upon
are	we
away	what
do	where
does	who
find	you
five	
for	
four	
go	
have	
he	
here	
I	
in	
is	
jump	
live	
me	
my	
not	
on	
once	
one	
pull	
said	
the	
they	
three	
to	
too	

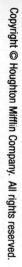

Decoding skills taught to date: *m, s, c, t,* short *a;* consonant *n;* consonant *f;* consonant *p;* short *i;* consonant *b;* consonant *r;* consonant *h;* consonant *g;* short *o;* consonant *d;* consonant *w;* consonant *l;* consonant *x;* short *e;* consonant *y;* consonant *k;* consonant *v;* short *u;* /kw/ spelled *qu;* consonant *j;* consonant *z;* /z/ spelled *s;* consonants *-ck;* /l/ spelled *-ll;* /f/ spelled *-ff;* /s/ spelled *-ss*

Jeff and Ruff

Here is the top!
Jeff and Ruff sit.

Jeff will go up a big hill.
His dog, Ruff, will go, too.

4

Jeff and Ruff go up.
Jeff has to lug a big pack.
Huff, puff. Huff, puff.

Jeff and Ruff go up, up, up.
Jeff and Ruff huff and puff.
Huff, puff. Huff, puff.
Huff, puff.

2

3

Can Jess Get a Bass?

DECODABLE WORDS

Target Skill: **/s/ spelled -ss**

bass   pass

Jess

Previously Taught Skills

can   has   net

get   his

SKILLS APPLIED IN WORDS IN STORY: *m, s, c, t*, short *a*; consonant *n*; consonant *p*;
short *i*; consonant *b*; consonant *h*; consonant *g*; short *e*; consonant *j*; /z/ spelled *s*

HIGH-FREQUENCY WORDS

a   here   the

are   jump   two

HOUGHTON MIFFLIN   BOSTON

Can Jess Get a Bass?

HIGH-FREQUENCY WORDS TAUGHT TO DATE

Grade 1

a	two
and	upon
are	we
away	what
do	where
does	who
find	you
five	
for	
four	
go	
have	
he	
here	
I	
in	
is	
jump	
live	
me	
my	
not	
on	
once	
one	
pull	
said	
the	
they	
three	
to	
too	

Decoding skills taught to date: m, s, c, t, short a; consonant n; consonant f; consonant p; short i; consonant b; consonant r; consonant h; consonant g; short o; consonant d; consonant w; consonant l; consonant x; short e; consonant y; consonant k; consonant v; short u; /kw/ spelled qu; consonant j; consonant z; /z/ spelled s; consonants -ck; /l/ spelled -ll; /f/ spelled -ff; /s/ spelled -ss

Can Jess Get a Bass?

Bass, bass, bass!

Here are two bass.

The bass jump.
Jess has a net.

Can Jess get a bass?
The bass pass his net.

2

3

The Ducks Quacked

DECODABLE WORDS

Target Skill: /t/ spelled -ed

passed   quacked
pecked

Previously Taught Skills

ducks   had   pen
fed   Jill

SKILLS APPLIED IN WORDS IN STORY: *m, s, c, t,* short *a*; consonant *n*; consonant *f*; consonant *p*; short *i*; consonant *h*; consonant *d*; short *e*; short *u*; /kw/ spelled *qu*; consonant *j*; consonants *-ck*; /l/ spelled *-ll*; /s/ spelled *-ss*

HIGH–FREQUENCY WORDS

a   the
go   to
of

HOUGHTON MIFFLIN   BOSTON

The Ducks Quacked

HIGH-FREQUENCY WORDS TAUGHT TO DATE

Grade 1

a	one
and	pull
animal	said
are	see
away	the
bird	they
cold	three
do	to
does	too
fall	two
find	upon
five	we
flower	what
for	where
four	who
full	you
go	
have	
he	
here	
I	
in	
is	
jump	
live	
look	
me	
my	
not	
of	
on	
once	

Decoding skills taught to date: m, s, c, t, short a; consonant n; consonant f; consonant p; short i; consonant b; consonant r; consonant h; consonant g; short o; consonant d; consonant w; consonant l; consonant x; short e; consonant y; consonant k; consonant v; short u; /kw/ spelled qu; consonant j; consonant z; /z/ spelled s; consonants -ck; /l/ spelled -ll; /f/ spelled -ff; /s/ spelled -ss; /t/ spelled -ed; /d/ spelled -ed; verb ending -ing

Jill had to go.

The ducks quacked,
quacked, quacked.

4

The Ducks Quacked

Jill passed a pen of ducks.

1

The ducks quacked,
quacked, quacked.

2

Jill fed the ducks.
The ducks pecked,
pecked, pecked.

3

Sis Yelled

DECODABLE WORDS

Target Skill: **/d/ spelled -ed**

filled
yelled

Previously Taught Skills

cup   Sis
Jon

SKILLS APPLIED IN WORDS IN STORY: *m, s, c, t,* short *a*; consonant *n*; consonant *f*;
consonant *p*; short *i*; short *o*; short *e*; consonant *y*; short *u*; consonant *j*; /l/ spelled *-ll*

HIGH–FREQUENCY WORDS

a   pulled
for

![Houghton Mifflin logo] HOUGHTON MIFFLIN   BOSTON

Sis Yelled

HIGH-FREQUENCY WORDS TAUGHT TO DATE

Grade 1

a	one
and	pull
animal	said
are	see
away	the
bird	they
cold	three
do	to
does	too
fall	two
find	upon
five	we
flower	what
for	where
four	who
full	you
go	
have	
he	
here	
I	
in	
is	
jump	
live	
look	
me	
my	
not	
of	
on	
once	

Decoding skills taught to date: *m, s, c, t,* short *a;* consonant *n;* consonant *f;* consonant *p;* short *i;* consonant *b;* consonant *r;* consonant *h;* consonant *g;* short *o;* consonant *d;* consonant *w;* consonant *l;* consonant *x;* short *e;* consonant *y;* consonant *k;* consonant *v;* short *u;* /kw/ spelled *qu;* consonant *j;* consonant *z;* /z/ spelled *s;* consonants *-ck;* /l/ spelled *-ll;* /f/ spelled *-ff;* /s/ spelled *-ss;* /t/ spelled *-ed;* /d/ spelled *-ed;* verb ending *-ing*

Sis yelled, yelled, yelled.

4

Sis Yelled

Jon pulled Sis. Sis yelled.

1

Sis yelled.

Sis yelled, yelled, yelled.

Jon filled a cup for Sis.

Fixing a Van

DECODABLE WORDS

Target Skill: verb ending –ing

buffing   fixing
filling   waxing

Previously Taught Skills

Hal   van
Hal's   wax

SKILLS APPLIED IN WORDS IN STORY: *m, s, c, t,* short *a*; consonant *n*; consonant *f*; short *i*; consonant *b*; consonant *h*; consonant *w*; consonant *l*; consonant *x*; consonant *v*; short *u*; /z/ spelled *s*; /l/ spelled *-ll*; /f/ spelled *-ff*

HIGH–FREQUENCY WORDS

a   pulling
and   the
is

HOUGHTON MIFFLIN   BOSTON

Fixing a Van

HIGH-FREQUENCY WORDS TAUGHT TO DATE

Grade 1

a	one
and	pull
animal	said
are	see
away	the
bird	they
cold	three
do	to
does	too
fall	two
find	upon
five	we
flower	what
for	where
four	who
full	you
go	
have	
he	
here	
I	
in	
is	
jump	
live	
look	
me	
my	
not	
of	
on	
once	

Decoding skills taught to date: *m, s, c, t,* short *a;* consonant *n;* consonant *f;* consonant *p;* short *i;* consonant *b;* consonant *r;* consonant *h;* consonant *g;* short *o;* consonant *d;* consonant *w;* consonant *l;* consonant *x;* short *e;* consonant *y;* consonant *k;* consonant *v;* short *u;* /kw/ spelled *qu;* consonant *j;* consonant *z;* /z/ spelled *s;* consonants *-ck;* /l/ spelled *-ll;* /f/ spelled *-ff;* /s/ spelled *-ss;* /t/ spelled *-ed;* /d/ spelled *-ed;* verb ending *-ing*

Hal is waxing and buffing the van.

4

Fixing a Van

Hal is pulling the van.

1

Hal is fixing the van.

Hal is filling the van.

Drips and Drops on Gran

DECODABLE WORDS

Target Skill: *r clusters*

brim	drop	from	grins
drip	drops	grabs	grips
drips	frog	Gran	trek

Previously Taught Skills

at	big	hops	will
bag	hat	wet	

SKILLS APPLIED IN WORDS IN STORY: *m, s, c, t,* short *a;* consonant *n;* consonant *f;* consonant *p;* short *i;* consonant *b;* consonant *r;* consonant *h;* consonant *g;* short *o;* consonant *d;* consonant *w;* short *e;* consonant *k;* /z/ spelled *s;* /l/ spelled -*ll*

HIGH-FREQUENCY WORDS

a	go	on
and	in	the
fall	of	

HOUGHTON MIFFLIN   BOSTON

Drips and Drops on Gran

HIGH-FREQUENCY WORDS TAUGHT TO DATE

Grade 1

a	my
all	never
and	not
animal	of
are	on
away	once
bird	one
call	paper
cold	pull
do	said
does	see
eat	shall
every	the
fall	they
find	three
first	to
five	too
flower	two
for	upon
four	we
full	what
go	where
have	who
he	why
here	you
I	
in	
is	
jump	
live	
look	
me	

Decoding skills taught to date: m, s, c, t, short a; consonant n; consonant f; consonant p; short i; consonant b; consonant r; consonant h; consonant g; short o; consonant d; consonant w; consonant l; consonant x; short e; consonant y; consonant k; consonant v; short u; /kw/ spelled qu; consonant j; consonant z; /z/ spelled s; consonants -ck; /l/ spelled -ll; /f/ spelled -ff; /s/ spelled -ss; /t/ spelled -ed; /d/ spelled -ed; verb ending -ing; r clusters

The frog hops in the wet
drips and drops.
Gran grins at the frog.

Drips and Drops on Gran

Gran will go on a trek.

Wet drips and drops
fall on Gran.
Gran grabs a big hat
from the bag.

Drip, drop, drip, drop, drip!
Gran grips the brim of
the big hat.

I ❤ LOVE READING BOOKS

THEME 4
Family and Friends

BOOK 32   The Duck Who Clucked

BOOK 33   Stan Sleds

BOOK 34   Can Yak Knit?

BOOK 35   Ren Wren Wraps

BOOK 36   Liz Gnat on a Trip

BOOK 37   Scrod Scraps for Cat

The Duck Who Clucked

DECODABLE WORDS

Target Skill: *l* **clusters**

cluck	clucks	flock
clucked	flap	

Previously Taught Skills

can	ducks	quack
duck	it	

SKILLS APPLIED IN WORDS IN STORY: *m, s, c, t,* short *a*; consonant *n*; consonant *f*; consonant *p*; short *i*; short *o*; consonant *d*; consonant *l*; short *u*; /kw/ spelled *qu*; /z/ spelled *s*; consonants *-ck*; /t/ spelled *-ed*

HIGH–FREQUENCY WORDS

a	is	the
and	not	too
in	one	who

The Duck Who Clucked

HOUGHTON MIFFLIN   BOSTON

HIGH-FREQUENCY WORDS TAUGHT TO DATE

Grade 1

a	in	you
all	is	
also	jump	
and	like	
animal	live	
are	look	
away	many	
bird	me	
blue	my	
brown	never	
call	not	
cold	of	
color	on	
do	once	
does	one	
eat	paper	
every	pull	
fall	said	
find	see	
first	shall	
five	some	
flower	the	
for	they	
four	three	
full	to	
funny	too	
go	two	
green	upon	
have	we	
he	what	
here	where	
I	who	
	why	

Decoding skills taught to date: m, s, c, t; short a; consonant n; consonant f; consonant p; short i; consonant b; consonant r; consonant h; consonant g; short o; consonant d; consonant w; consonant l; consonant x; short e; consonant y; consonant k; consonant v; short u; /kw/ spelled qu; consonant j; consonant z; /z/ spelled s; consonants -ck; /l/ spelled -ll; /f/ spelled -ff; /s/ spelled -ss; /t/ spelled -ed; /d/ spelled -ed; verb ending -ing; r clusters; l clusters

The flock can quack **and** cluck.

Quack, quack, cluck!

4

The Duck Who Clucked

Ducks in the flock flap.

Flap, flap, flap.

1

Ducks in the flock quack, too.
Flap, quack. Flap, quack.
Flap, quack.

One duck clucks, "Cluck,
cluck, cluck."
It is not a duck! Ducks quack!

2

3

Stan Sleds

DECODABLE WORDS

Target Skill: _s clusters_

sled	slid	spot	still
sleds	sped	Stan	stuck

Previously Taught Skills

flat	hill	it
has	his	

SKILLS APPLIED IN WORDS IN STORY: *m, s, c, t,* short *a;* consonant *n;* consonant *f;* consonant *p;* short *i;* consonant *h;* short *o;* consonant *d;* consonant *l;* short *e;* short *u;* /z/ spelled *s;* consonants *-ck;* /l/ spelled *-ll; l* clusters

HIGH-FREQUENCY WORDS

a	is	the
and	not	too
here	on	

HOUGHTON MIFFLIN   BOSTON

Stan Sleds

HIGH-FREQUENCY WORDS TAUGHT TO DATE

Grade 1

a	have	too
all	he	two
also	here	upon
and	I	we
animal	in	what
are	is	where
away	jump	who
bird	like	why
blue	live	you
brown	look	your
call	love	
children	many	
cold	me	
color	mother	
come	my	
do	never	
does	not	
eat	of	
every	on	
fall	once	
family	one	
father	paper	
find	people	
first	picture	
five	pull	
flower	said	
for	see	
four	shall	
full	some	
funny	the	
go	they	
green	three	
	to	

Decoding skills taught to date: *m, s, c, t,* short *a;* consonant *n;* consonant *f;* consonant *p;* short *i;* consonant *b;* consonant *r;* consonant *h;* consonant *g;* short *o;* consonant *d;* consonant *w;* consonant *l;* consonant *x;* short *e;* consonant *y;* consonant *k;* consonant *v;* short *u;* /kw/ spelled *qu;* consonant *j;* consonant *z;* /z/ spelled *s;* consonants *-ck;* /l/ spelled *-ll;* /f/ spelled *-ff;* /s/ spelled *-ss;* /t/ spelled *-ed;* /d/ spelled *-ed;* verb ending *-ing; r* clusters; *l* clusters; *s* clusters; silent *k* in *kn;* silent *w* in *wr;* silent *g* in *gn*

Stan Sleds

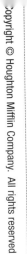

Stan slid and sped on his sled.

4

Stan has a sled.

It is stuck.

1

The sled is still stuck.
The hill is too flat here.

The spot here is not too flat!

Can Yak Knit?

DECODABLE WORDS

Target Skill: silent *k* in *kn*

knack	knot
knit	

Previously Taught Skills

big	get	it	yes
can	gets	Yak	yet

SKILLS APPLIED IN WORDS IN STORY: *m, s, c, t,* short *a*; consonant *n*; short *i*; consonant *b*; consonant *g*; short *o*; short *e*; consonant *y*; consonant *k*; consonants *-ck*

HIGH-FREQUENCY WORDS

a	not
does	of
have	the

Can Yak Knit?

HIGH-FREQUENCY WORDS TAUGHT TO DATE

Grade 1

a	have	too
all	he	two
also	here	upon
and	I	we
animal	in	what
are	is	where
away	jump	who
bird	like	why
blue	live	you
brown	look	your
call	love	
children	many	
cold	me	
color	mother	
come	my	
do	never	
does	not	
eat	of	
every	on	
fall	once	
family	one	
father	paper	
find	people	
first	picture	
five	pull	
flower	said	
for	see	
four	shall	
full	some	
funny	the	
go	they	
green	three	
	to	

Decoding skills taught to date: m, s, c, t, short a; consonant n; consonant f; consonant p; short i; consonant b; consonant r; consonant h; consonant g; short o; consonant d; consonant w; consonant l; consonant x; short e; consonant y; consonant k; consonant v; short u; /kw/ spelled qu; consonant j; consonant z; /z/ spelled s; consonants -ck; /l/ spelled -ll; /f/ spelled -ff; /s/ spelled -ss; /t/ spelled -ed; /d/ spelled -ed; verb ending -ing; r clusters; l clusters; s clusters; silent k in kn; silent w in wr; silent g in gn

Can Yak Knit?

Can Yak knit?

1

Yes! Yak can knit.

Knit, knit, knit.

4

Yak gets a big knot.
Yak does not have the
knack yet.

Can Yak get the knack of it?

Ren Wren Wraps

HOUGHTON MIFFLIN   BOSTON

Ren Wren Wraps

HIGH-FREQUENCY WORDS TAUGHT TO DATE

Grade 1

a	have	too
all	he	two
also	here	upon
and	I	we
animal	in	what
are	is	where
away	jump	who
bird	like	why
blue	live	you
brown	look	your
call	love	
children	many	
cold	me	
color	mother	
come	my	
do	never	
does	not	
eat	of	
every	on	
fall	once	
family	one	
father	paper	
find	people	
first	picture	
five	pull	
flower	said	
for	see	
four	shall	
full	some	
funny	the	
go	they	
green	three	
	to	

Decoding skills taught to date: *m, s, c, t,* short *a;* consonant *n;* consonant *f;* consonant *p;* short *i;* consonant *b;* consonant *r;* consonant *h;* consonant *g;* short *o;* consonant *d;* consonant *w;* consonant *l;* consonant *x;* short *e;* consonant *y;* consonant *k;* consonant *v;* short *u;* /kw/ spelled *qu;* consonant *j;* consonant *z;* /z/ spelled *s;* consonants *-ck;* /l/ spelled *-ll;* /f/ spelled *-ff;* /s/ spelled *-ss;* /t/ spelled *-ed;* /d/ spelled *-ed;* verb ending *-ing;* *r* clusters; *l* clusters; *s* clusters; silent *k* in *kn;* silent *w* in *wr;* silent *g* in *gn*

The box is for Ron Wren.

4

Ren Wren Wraps

Ren Wren has a box.

1

Ren Wren wraps the box.

Ren Wren has a tag.

Liz Gnat on a Trip

DECODABLE WORDS

Target Skill: silent *g* in *gn*

gnat

Previously Taught Skills

back	has	sits	trip
fun	Liz	sun	will

SKILLS APPLIED IN WORDS IN STORY: *m, s, c, t,* short *a;* consonant *n;* consonant *f;* consonant *p;* short *i;* consonant *b;* consonant *r;* consonant *h;* short *o;* consonant *w;* consonant *l;* consonant *k;* short *u;* consonant *z;* /z/ spelled *s;* consonants *-ck;* /l/ spelled *-ll; r* clusters

HIGH–FREQUENCY WORDS

a	is
go	on
in	the

HOUGHTON MIFFLIN   BOSTON

Liz Gnat on a Trip

HIGH-FREQUENCY WORDS TAUGHT TO DATE

Grade 1

a	have	too
all	he	two
also	here	upon
and	I	we
animal	in	what
are	is	where
away	jump	who
bird	like	why
blue	live	you
brown	look	your
call	love	
children	many	
cold	me	
color	mother	
come	my	
do	never	
does	not	
eat	of	
every	on	
fall	once	
family	one	
father	paper	
find	people	
first	picture	
five	pull	
flower	said	
for	see	
four	shall	
full	some	
funny	the	
go	they	
green	three	
	to	

Decoding skills taught to date: *m, s, c, t,* short *a;* consonant *n;* consonant *f;* consonant *p;* short *i;* consonant *b;* consonant *r;* consonant *h;* consonant *g;* short *o;* consonant *d;* consonant *w;* consonant *l;* consonant *x;* short *e;* consonant *y;* consonant *k;* consonant *v;* short *u;* /kw/ spelled *qu;* consonant *j;* consonant *z;* /z/ spelled *s;* consonants *-ck;* /l/ spelled *-ll;* /f/ spelled *-ff;* /s/ spelled *-ss;* /t/ spelled *-ed;* /d/ spelled *-ed;* verb ending *-ing;* *r* clusters; *l* clusters; *s* clusters; silent *k* in *kn;* silent *w* in *wr;* silent *g* in *gn*

Liz Gnat will go back.

4

Liz Gnat on a Trip

Liz Gnat is on a trip.

1

Liz Gnat sits in the sun.

2

Liz Gnat has fun.

3

Scrod Scraps for Cat

DECODABLE WORDS

Target Skill: triple clusters

scram   scrod

scraps   splat

Previously Taught Skills

asked   Cat   fed

can   Dad   Sal

SKILLS APPLIED IN WORDS IN STORY: *m, s, c, t,* short *a*; consonant *n*; consonant *f*; consonant *p*; consonant *r*; short *o*; consonant *d*; consonant *l*; short *e*; consonant *k*; /t/ spelled *-ed*; *s* clusters

HIGH–FREQUENCY WORDS

for   see

have   some

said

triple clusters

BOOK 37

Scrod Scraps for Cat

HIGH-FREQUENCY WORDS TAUGHT TO DATE

Grade 1

a	go	she
all	green	sing
also	have	some
and	he	the
animal	here	they
are	I	three
away	in	to
bird	is	today
blue	jump	too
brown	know	two
call	like	upon
children	live	we
cold	look	what
color	love	where
come	many	who
do	me	why
does	mother	write
eat	my	you
every	never	your
fall	not	
family	of	
father	on	
find	once	
first	one	
five	paper	
flower	people	
for	picture	
four	play	
friend	pull	
full	read	
funny	said	
girl	see	
	shall	

Decoding skills taught to date: m, s, c, t, short a; consonant n; consonant f; consonant p; short i; consonant b; consonant r; consonant h; consonant g; short o; consonant d; consonant w; consonant l; consonant x; short e; consonant y; consonant k; consonant v; short u; /kw/ spelled qu; consonant j; consonant z; /z/ spelled s; consonants -ck; /l/ spelled -ll; /f/ spelled -ff; /s/ spelled -ss; /t/ spelled -ed; /d/ spelled -ed; verb ending -ing; r clusters; l clusters; s clusters; silent k in kn; silent w in wr; silent g in gn; triple clusters

Sal fed Cat some scrod scraps.

4

Scrod Scraps for Cat

Cat can see some scrod scraps.

1

Splat! "Scram, Cat!" said Dad.

"Can Cat have some scrod scraps, Dad?" asked Sal.

"Liz Gnat is away!"
Jon Gnat sobs.

Liz Gnat is back!

Jon Gnat

Jon Gnat is sad.

1

Jon Gnat is glad.

4

HIGH-FREQUENCY WORDS TAUGHT TO DATE

Grade 1

a	funny	play
all	girl	pull
also	go	read
and	green	said
animal	have	see
are	he	shall
away	hear	she
bird	here	sing
blue	hold	some
brown	hurt	the
call	I	their
car	in	they
children	is	three
cold	jump	to
color	know	today
come	learn	too
do	like	two
does	live	upon
down	look	walk
eat	love	we
every	many	what
fall	me	where
family	mother	who
father	my	why
find	never	would
first	not	write
five	of	you
flower	on	your
for	once	
four	one	
friend	paper	
full	people	
	picture	

Decoding skills taught to date: *m, s, c, t,* short *a;* consonant *n;* consonant *f;* consonant *p;* short *i;* consonant *b;* consonant *r;* consonant *h;* consonant *g;* short *o;* consonant *d;* consonant *w;* consonant *l;* consonant *x;* short *e;* consonant *y;* consonant *k;* consonant *v;* short *u;* /kw/ spelled *qu;* consonant *j;* consonant *z;* /z/ spelled *s;* consonants *-ck;* /l/ spelled *-ll;* /f/ spelled *-ff;* /s/ spelled *-ss;* /t/ spelled *-ed;* /d/ spelled *-ed;* verb ending *-ing;* *r* clusters; *l* clusters; *s* clusters; silent *k* in *kn;* silent *w* in *wr;* silent *g* in *gn;* triple clusters

Jon Gnat

DECODABLE WORDS

Target Skill: silent *g* in *gn*

gnat

Previously Taught Skills

back	Jon	sad
glad	Liz	sobs

SKILLS APPLIED IN WORDS IN STORY: *m, s, c, t,* short *a*; consonant *n*; short *i*; consonant *b*; consonant *g*; short *o*; consonant *d*; consonant *l*; consonant *k*; consonant *j*; consonant *z*; /z/ spelled *s*; consonants -*ck*; *l* clusters

HIGH–FREQUENCY WORDS

away

is

HOUGHTON MIFFLIN BOSTON

Jon Gnat

Ren Wren writes a lot.

Ben Wren has a pen.
Ben Wren writes a lot, too!

"Mom! Ben Wren
wrecked it!"

4

Ren Wren Writes

Ren Wren has a pen.
Ren Wren writes.

1

HIGH-FREQUENCY WORDS TAUGHT TO DATE

Grade 1

a	funny	play
all	girl	pull
also	go	read
and	green	said
animal	have	see
are	he	shall
away	hear	she
bird	here	sing
blue	hold	some
brown	hurt	the
call	I	their
car	in	they
children	is	three
cold	jump	to
color	know	today
come	learn	too
do	like	two
does	live	upon
down	look	walk
eat	love	we
every	many	what
fall	me	where
family	mother	who
father	my	why
find	never	would
first	not	write
five	of	you
flower	on	your
for	once	
four	one	
friend	paper	
full	people	
	picture	

Decoding skills taught to date: m, s, c, t, short a; consonant n; consonant f; consonant p; short i; consonant b; consonant r; consonant h; consonant g; short o; consonant d; consonant w; consonant l; consonant x; short e; consonant y; consonant k; consonant v; short u; /kw/ spelled qu; consonant j; consonant z; /z/ spelled s; consonants -ck; /l/ spelled -ll; /f/ spelled -ff; /s/ spelled -ss; /t/ spelled -ed; /d/ spelled -ed; verb ending -ing; r clusters; l clusters; s clusters; silent k in kn; silent w in wr; silent g in gn; triple clusters

DECODABLE WORDS

Target Skill: silent *w* in *wr*

wrecked
Wren

Previously Taught Skills

Ben	has	lot	pen
can	it	Mom	Ren

SKILLS APPLIED IN WORDS IN STORY: *m, s, c, t,* short *a;* consonant *n;* consonant *p;* short *i;* consonant *b;* consonant *r;* consonant *h;* short *o;* consonant *l;* short *e;* consonants *-ck;* /t/ spelled *-ed*

HIGH–FREQUENCY WORDS

a	too	writes
I	write	

HOUGHTON MIFFLIN   BOSTON

Ren Wren Writes

Gran knits and knits.
Gran knows Ben is knocking.

"Grab the knob, Ben!" Gran calls.
Ben grabs the knob.

Ben can help Gran knit.

Knit, knit, knit.

4

Ben Knocks, Gran Knits

Ben knocks.

Knock, knock, knock.

1

HIGH-FREQUENCY WORDS TAUGHT TO DATE

Grade 1

a	funny	play
all	girl	pull
also	go	read
and	green	said
animal	have	see
are	he	shall
away	hear	she
bird	here	sing
blue	hold	some
brown	hurt	the
call	I	their
car	in	they
children	is	three
cold	jump	to
color	know	today
come	learn	too
do	like	two
does	live	upon
down	look	walk
eat	love	we
every	many	what
fall	me	where
family	mother	who
father	my	why
find	never	would
first	not	write
five	of	you
flower	on	your
for	once	
four	one	
friend	paper	
full	people	
	picture	

Decoding skills taught to date: *m, s, c, t,* short *a;* consonant *n;* consonant *f;* consonant *p;* short *i;* consonant *b;* consonant *r;* consonant *h;* consonant *g;* short *o;* consonant *d;* consonant *w;* consonant *l;* consonant *x;* short *e;* consonant *y;* consonant *k;* consonant *v;* short *u;* /kw/ spelled *qu;* consonant *j;* consonant *z;* /z/ spelled *s;* consonants *-ck;* /l/ spelled *-ll;* /f/ spelled *-ff;* /s/ spelled *-ss;* /t/ spelled *-ed;* /d/ spelled *-ed;* verb ending *-ing;* *r* clusters; *l* clusters; *s* clusters; silent *k* in *kn;* silent *w* in *wr;* silent *g* in *gn;* triple clusters

Ben Knocks, Gran Knits

DECODABLE WORDS

Target Skill: silent *k* in *kn*

knit	knob	knocking
knits	knock	knocks

Previously Taught Skills

Ben	grab	Gran
can	grabs	help

SKILLS APPLIED IN WORDS IN STORY: *m, s, c, t*, short *a*; consonant *n*; consonant *p*; short *i*; consonant *b*; consonant *r*; consonant *h*; consonant *g*; short *o*; short *e*; /z/ spelled *s*; consonants -*ck*; verb ending -*ing*; *r* clusters

HIGH–FREQUENCY WORDS

and	knows
calls	the
is	

HOUGHTON MIFFLIN   BOSTON

Ben Knocks, Gran Knits

Will Spot snag the snack?

2

Stop, Spot!
Stop, stop, stop!

3

Spot can have a dog snack.

4

Spot Smells a Snack

Spot can smell a snack.
Sniff, sniff, sniff.

1

HIGH-FREQUENCY WORDS TAUGHT TO DATE

Grade 1

a	funny	play
all	girl	pull
also	go	read
and	green	said
animal	have	see
are	he	shall
away	hear	she
bird	here	sing
blue	hold	some
brown	hurt	the
call	I	their
car	in	they
children	is	three
cold	jump	to
color	know	today
come	learn	too
do	like	two
does	live	upon
down	look	walk
eat	love	we
every	many	what
fall	me	where
family	mother	who
father	my	why
find	never	would
first	not	write
five	of	you
flower	on	your
for	once	
four	one	
friend	paper	
full	people	
	picture	

Decoding skills taught to date: m, s, c, t, short a; consonant n; consonant f; consonant p; short i; consonant b; consonant r; consonant h; consonant g; short o; consonant d; consonant w; consonant l; consonant x; short e; consonant y; consonant k; consonant v; short u; /kw/ spelled qu; consonant j; consonant z; /z/ spelled s; consonants -ck; /l/ spelled -ll; /f/ spelled -ff; /s/ spelled -ss; /t/ spelled -ed; /d/ spelled -ed; verb ending -ing; r clusters; l clusters; s clusters; silent k in kn; silent w in wr; silent g in gn; triple clusters

Spot Smells a Snack

DECODABLE WORDS

Target Skill: *s clusters*

smell	snack	sniff	stop
smells	snag	Spot	

Previously Taught Skills

can	will
dog	

SKILLS APPLIED IN WORDS IN STORY: *m, s, c, t,* short *a*; consonant *n*; consonant *f*; consonant *p*; short *i*; consonant *g*; short *o*; consonant *d*; consonant *w*; consonant *l*; short *e*; /z/ spelled *s*; consonants *-ck*; /l/ spelled *-ll*; /f/ spelled *-ff*

HIGH–FREQUENCY WORDS

a	the
have	

Spot Smells a Snack

HOUGHTON MIFFLIN   BOSTON

Here is Clem!

Clip, clop, clip, clop.

The drums go clack clack.

Clack, clack, clack.

We are glad. We clap.

Clap, clap, clap.

We Clap

Fran has a flag.

The flag flaps.

Flap, flap, flap.

HIGH-FREQUENCY WORDS TAUGHT TO DATE

Grade 1

a	go	she
all	green	sing
also	have	some
and	he	the
animal	here	they
are	I	three
away	in	to
bird	is	today
blue	jump	too
brown	know	two
call	like	upon
children	live	we
cold	look	what
color	love	where
come	many	who
do	me	why
does	mother	write
eat	my	you
every	never	your
fall	not	
family	of	
father	on	
find	once	
first	one	
five	paper	
flower	people	
for	picture	
four	play	
friend	pull	
full	read	
funny	said	
girl	see	
	shall	

Decoding skills taught to date: *m, s, c, t,* short *a;* consonant *n;* consonant *f;* consonant *p;* short *i;* consonant *b;* consonant *r;* consonant *h;* consonant *g;* short *o;* consonant *d;* consonant *w;* consonant *l;* consonant *x;* short *e;* consonant *y;* consonant *k;* consonant *v;* short *u;* /kw/ spelled *qu;* consonant *j;* consonant *z;* /z/ spelled *s;* consonants *-ck;* /l/ spelled *-ll;* /f/ spelled *-ff;* /s/ spelled *-ss;* /t/ spelled *-ed;* /d/ spelled *-ed;* verb ending *-ing;* *r* clusters; *l* clusters; *s* clusters; silent *k* in *kn;* silent *w* in *wr;* silent *g* in *gn*

We Clap

DECODABLE WORDS

Target Skill: l clusters

clack	Clem	clop	flap	glad
clap	clip	flag	flaps	

Previously Taught Skills

drums   has
Fran

SKILLS APPLIED IN WORDS IN STORY: *m, s, c, t,* short *a;* consonant *n;* consonant *f;* consonant *p;* short *i;* consonant *r;* consonant *h;* consonant *g;* short *o;* consonant *d;* consonant *l;* short *e;* short *u; /z/* spelled *s;* consonants *-ck; r* clusters

HIGH-FREQUENCY WORDS

a	go	is	we
are	here	the	

We Clap

HOUGHTON MIFFLIN   BOSTON

Fred is filling the crack.

2

Brad grips the drill.
He is drilling the rods.

3

Fran, Fred, and Brad Fix It

Drip, drop, drip, drop.
Fran is fixing the drip.

Fran, Fred, and Brad pull
the bricks.

HIGH-FREQUENCY WORDS TAUGHT TO DATE

Grade 1

a	have	too
all	he	two
also	here	upon
and	I	we
animal	in	what
are	is	where
away	jump	who
bird	like	why
blue	live	you
brown	look	your
call	love	
children	many	
cold	me	
color	mother	
come	my	
do	never	
does	not	
eat	of	
every	on	
fall	once	
family	one	
father	paper	
find	people	
first	picture	
five	pull	
flower	said	
for	see	
four	shall	
full	some	
funny	the	
go	they	
green	three	
	to	

Decoding skills taught to date: m, s, c, t, short a; consonant n; consonant f; consonant p; short i; consonant b; consonant r; consonant h; consonant g; short o; consonant d; consonant w; consonant l; consonant x; short e; consonant y; consonant k; consonant v; short u; /kw/ spelled qu; consonant j; consonant z; /z/ spelled s; consonants -ck; /l/ spelled -ll; /f/ spelled -ff; /s/ spelled -ss; /t/ spelled -ed; /d/ spelled -ed; verb ending -ing; r clusters; l clusters

Fran, Fred, and Brad Fix It

DECODABLE WORDS

Target Skill: *r* clusters

Brad	crack	drilling	drop	Fred
bricks	drill	drip	Fran	grips

Previously Taught Skills

filling	fixing	rods
fix	it	

SKILLS APPLIED IN WORDS IN STORY: *m, s, c, t,* short *a*; consonant *n*; consonant *f*; consonant *p*; short *i*; consonant *b*; consonant *r*; consonant *g*; short *o*; consonant *d*; consonant *x*; short *e*; /z/ spelled *s*; consonants *-ck*; /l/ spelled *-ll*; verb ending *–ing*

HIGH–FREQUENCY WORDS

and	is	the
he	pull	

HOUGHTON MIFFLIN   BOSTON

Fran, Fred, and Brad
Fix It

I LOVE READING BOOKS

THEME 4
Family and Friends

REVIEW BOOK 31   Fran, Fred, and Brad Fix It
REVIEW BOOK 32   We Clap
REVIEW BOOK 33   Spot Smells a Snack
REVIEW BOOK 34   Ben Knocks, Gran Knits
REVIEW BOOK 35   Ren Wren Writes
REVIEW BOOK 36   Jon Gnat

Val is calling.
Cat is hissing.

Cat is jumping.

Val is rocking Cat.

Cat is licking Val.

4

Cat Is Missing!

Cat is missing!

1

HIGH-FREQUENCY WORDS TAUGHT TO DATE

Grade 1

a	in	you
all	is	
also	jump	
and	like	
animal	live	
are	look	
away	many	
bird	me	
blue	my	
brown	never	
call	not	
cold	of	
color	on	
do	once	
does	one	
eat	paper	
every	pull	
fall	said	
find	see	
first	shall	
five	some	
flower	the	
for	they	
four	three	
full	to	
funny	too	
go	two	
green	upon	
have	we	
he	what	
here	where	
I	who	
	why	

Decoding skills taught to date: *m, s, c, t,* short *a;* consonant *n;* consonant *f;* consonant *p;* short *i;* consonant *b;* consonant *r;* consonant *h;* consonant *g;* short *o;* consonant *d;* consonant *w;* consonant *l;* consonant *x;* short *e;* consonant *y;* consonant *k;* consonant *v;* short *u;* /kw/ spelled *qu;* consonant *j;* consonant *z;* /z/ spelled *s;* consonants *-ck;* /l/ spelled *-ll;* /f/ spelled *-ff;* /s/ spelled *-ss;* /t/ spelled *-ed;* /d/ spelled *-ed;* verb ending *-ing;* *r* clusters

Cat Is Missing!

DECODABLE WORDS

Target Skill: verb ending *–ing*

hissing   missing
licking   rocking

Previously Taught Skills

Cat
Val

SKILLS APPLIED IN WORDS IN STORY: *m, s, c, t,* short *a;* short *i;* consonant *r;* consonant *h;* short *o;* consonant *l;* consonant *v;* /z/ spelled *s;* consonants *-ck;* /s/ spelled *-ss*

HIGH–FREQUENCY WORDS

calling   jumping
is

HOUGHTON MIFFLIN   BOSTON

Cat Is Missing!

Ron filled a can.

Rex Dog sat.

Ron filled, filled, filled.

He had a big, big hill.

Rex Dog sat.

Rex Dog sat!

"Do not sit on the hill, Rex!"

Ron yelled, yelled, yelled.

4

Ron Filled

Ron filled a pot.

Rex Dog sat.

1

HIGH-FREQUENCY WORDS TAUGHT TO DATE

Grade 1	in	you
a	is	
all	jump	
also	like	
and	live	
animal	look	
are	many	
away	me	
bird	my	
blue	never	
brown	not	
call	of	
cold	on	
color	once	
do	one	
does	paper	
eat	pull	
every	said	
fall	see	
find	shall	
first	some	
five	the	
flower	they	
for	three	
four	to	
full	too	
funny	two	
go	upon	
green	we	
have	what	
he	where	
here	who	
I	why	

Decoding skills taught to date: *m, s, c, t,* short *a;* consonant *n;* consonant *f;* consonant *p;* short *i;* consonant *b;* consonant *r;* consonant *h;* consonant *g;* short *o;* consonant *d;* consonant *w;* consonant *l;* consonant *x;* short *e;* consonant *y;* consonant *k;* consonant *v;* short *u;* /kw/ spelled *qu;* consonant *j;* consonant *z;* /z/ spelled *s;* consonants *-ck;* /l/ spelled *-ll;* /f/ spelled *-ff;* /s/ spelled *-ss;* /t/ spelled *-ed;* /d/ spelled *-ed;* verb ending *-ing; r* clusters

Ron Filled

DECODABLE WORDS

Target Skill: /d/ spelled -*ed*

filled
yelled

Previously Taught Skills

big	Dog	hill	Rex	sat
can	had	pot	Ron	sit

SKILLS APPLIED IN WORDS IN STORY: *m, s, c, t,* short *a*; consonant *n*; consonant *f*; consonant *p*; short *i*; consonant *b*; consonant *r*; consonant *h*; consonant *g*; short *o*; consonant *d*; consonant *l*; consonant *x*; short *e*; consonant *y*; /l/ spelled -*ll*

HIGH–FREQUENCY WORDS

a	he	on
do	not	the

HOUGHTON MIFFLIN   BOSTON

Ron Filled

The pigs locked the hut.
The hut rocked, but it did not fall.

Big Bad Mac jumped.

Mac Missed

Big Bad Mac huffed and puffed.

Big Bad Mac missed.

Big Bad Mac fell.

4

1

HIGH-FREQUENCY WORDS TAUGHT TO DATE

Grade 1

	in	you
a	is	
all	jump	
also	like	
and	live	
animal	look	
are	many	
away	me	
bird	my	
blue	never	
brown	not	
call	of	
cold	on	
color	once	
do	one	
does	paper	
eat	pull	
every	said	
fall	see	
find	shall	
first	some	
five	the	
flower	they	
for	three	
four	to	
full	too	
funny	two	
go	upon	
green	we	
have	what	
he	where	
here	who	
I	why	

Decoding skills taught to date: m, s, c, t, short *a*; consonant *n*; consonant *f*; consonant *p*; short *i*; consonant *b*; consonant *r*; consonant *h*; consonant *g*; short *o*; consonant *d*; consonant *w*; consonant *l*; consonant *x*; short *e*; consonant *y*; consonant *k*; consonant *v*; short *u*; /kw/ spelled *qu*; consonant *j*; consonant *z*; /z/ spelled *s*; consonants -*ck*; /l/ spelled -*ll*; /f/ spelled -*ff*; /s/ spelled -*ss*; /t/ spelled -*ed*; /d/ spelled -*ed*; verb ending -*ing*; *r* clusters

Mac Missed

DECODABLE WORDS

Target Skill: /t/ spelled -ed

huffed	missed	rocked
locked	puffed	

Previously Taught Skills

bad	did	it
big	fell	Mac
but	hut	pigs

SKILLS APPLIED IN WORDS IN STORY: *m, s, c, t,* short *a;* consonant *n;* consonant *f;* consonant *p;* short *i;* consonant *b;* consonant *r;* consonant *h;* consonant *g;* short *o;* consonant *d;* consonant *l;* short *e;* short *u;* /z/ spelled *s;* consonants *-ck;* /l/ spelled *-ll;* /f/ spelled *-ff;* /s/ spelled *-ss*

HIGH–FREQUENCY WORDS

and	jumped	the
fall	not	

HOUGHTON MIFFLIN   BOSTON

Mac Missed

"We can get a cup, Tess,"
said Bess.
"Yes, Bess!" said Tess.

Tess passed Bess a cup.

"It is for you, Mom,"
said Bess and Tess.
Tess and Bess got a kiss.
Kiss! Kiss!

4

Tess and Bess

"We can pick a flower, Bess,"
said Tess.
"Yes, Tess!" said Bess.

1

HIGH-FREQUENCY WORDS TAUGHT TO DATE

Grade 1

a	my
all	never
and	not
animal	of
are	on
away	once
bird	one
call	paper
cold	pull
do	said
does	see
eat	shall
every	the
fall	they
find	three
first	to
five	too
flower	two
for	upon
four	we
full	what
go	where
have	who
he	why
here	you
I	
in	
is	
jump	
live	
look	
me	

Decoding skills taught to date: *m, s, c, t,* short *a;* consonant *n;* consonant *f;* consonant *p;* short *i;* consonant *b;* consonant *r;* consonant *h;* consonant *g;* short *o;* consonant *d;* consonant *w;* consonant *l;* consonant *x;* short *e;* consonant *y;* consonant *k;* consonant *v;* short *u;* /kw/ spelled *qu;* consonant *j;* consonant *z;* /z/ spelled *s;* consonants *-ck;* /l/ spelled *-ll;* /f/ spelled *-ff;* /s/ spelled *-ss;* /t/ spelled *-ed;* /d/ spelled *-ed;* verb ending *-ing*

Tess and Bess

DECODABLE WORDS

Target Skill: /s/ spelled -ss

Bess	passed
kiss	Tess

Previously Taught Skills

can	get	it	pick
cup	got	Mom	yes

SKILLS APPLIED IN WORDS IN STORY: *m, s, c, t,* short *a*; consonant *n*; consonant *p*; short *i*; consonant *b*; consonant *g*; short *o*; short *e*; consonant *y*; consonant *k*; short *u*; /z/ spelled *s*; consonants *-ck*; /t/ spelled *-ed*

HIGH–FREQUENCY WORDS

a	flower	is	we
and	for	said	you

HOUGHTON MIFFLIN   BOSTON

Tess and Bess

The muff is not on.

Liz is not hot.

It is a big, cold puff!

Liz can see the muff go up, up, up!

Muff in a Puff!

Liz has a muff on.

The muff is too hot.

Liz can not find the muff.

Can you see the muff?

4

1

HIGH-FREQUENCY WORDS TAUGHT TO DATE

Grade 1

a	my
all	never
and	not
animal	of
are	on
away	once
bird	one
call	paper
cold	pull
do	said
does	see
eat	shall
every	the
fall	they
find	three
first	to
five	too
flower	two
for	upon
four	we
full	what
go	where
have	who
he	why
here	you
I	
in	
is	
jump	
live	
look	
me	

Decoding skills taught to date: *m, s, c, t,* short *a;* consonant *n;* consonant *f;* consonant *p;* short *i;* consonant *b;* consonant *r;* consonant *h;* consonant *g;* short *o;* consonant *d;* consonant *w;* consonant *l;* consonant *x;* short *e;* consonant *y;* consonant *k;* consonant *v;* short *u;* /kw/ spelled *qu;* consonant *j;* consonant *z;* /z/ spelled *s;* consonants *-ck;* /l/ spelled *-ll;* /f/ spelled *-ff;* /s/ spelled *-ss;* /t/ spelled *-ed;* /d/ spelled *-ed;* verb ending *-ing*

Muff in a Puff!

DECODABLE WORDS

Target Skill: /f/ spelled -ff

muff
puff

Previously Taught Skills

big	has	it	up
can	hot	Liz	

SKILLS APPLIED IN WORDS IN STORY: *m, s, c, t,* short *a*; consonant *n*; consonant *f*; consonant *p*; short *i*; consonant *b*; consonant *h*; consonant *g*; short *o*; consonant *l*; short *u*; consonant *z*; /z/ spelled *s*

HIGH-FREQUENCY WORDS

a	go	not	the
cold	in	on	too
find	is	see	you

HOUGHTON MIFFLIN   BOSTON

Muff in a Puff!

Jill tossed to Bill.

"Get it, Bill," said Jill.

Bill and Jill ran, ran, ran.

Bill and Jill got hot, hot, hot.

Bill and Jill

Jill filled a pan for Bill.

Jill filled a cup, too!

4

Jill ran on a hill.

Bill ran on the hill, too!

1

HIGH-FREQUENCY WORDS TAUGHT TO DATE

Grade 1

a	my
all	never
and	not
animal	of
are	on
away	once
bird	one
call	paper
cold	pull
do	said
does	see
eat	shall
every	the
fall	they
find	three
first	to
five	too
flower	two
for	upon
four	we
full	what
go	where
have	who
he	why
here	you
I	
in	
is	
jump	
live	
look	
me	

Decoding skills taught to date: m, s, c, t, short a; consonant n; consonant f; consonant p; short i; consonant b; consonant r; consonant h; consonant g; short o; consonant d; consonant w; consonant l; consonant x; short e; consonant y; consonant k; consonant v; short u; /kw/ spelled qu; consonant j; consonant z; /z/ spelled s; consonants -ck; /l/ spelled -ll; /f/ spelled -ff; /s/ spelled -ss; /t/ spelled -ed; /d/ spelled -ed; verb ending -ing

Bill and Jill

DECODABLE WORDS

Target Skill: /l/ spelled -ll

Bill	hill
filled	Jill

Previously Taught Skills

cup	got	it	ran
get	hot	pan	tossed

SKILLS APPLIED IN WORDS IN STORY: *m, s, c, t,* short *a*; consonant *n*; consonant *f*; consonant *p*; short *i*; consonant *b*; consonant *r*; consonant *h*; consonant *g*; short *o*; short *e*; short *u*; consonant *j*; /s/ spelled -*ss*; /t/ spelled -*ed*; /d/ spelled -*ed*

HIGH–FREQUENCY WORDS

a	for	said	to
and	on	the	too

HOUGHTON MIFFLIN   BOSTON

Bill and Jill

Rick said, "Jack, are you sick?"
Jack said, "Quack."

2

Rick said, "I can tug you, Jack."
Jack said, "Quack! Quack!"

3

"Quack! Quack! Quack!"

Jack the Duck

Jack is a duck.

Jack sat on a dock.

HIGH-FREQUENCY WORDS TAUGHT TO DATE

Grade 1

a	my
all	never
and	not
animal	of
are	on
away	once
bird	one
call	paper
cold	pull
do	said
does	see
eat	shall
every	the
fall	they
find	three
first	to
five	too
flower	two
for	upon
four	we
full	what
go	where
have	who
he	why
here	you
I	
in	
is	
jump	
live	
look	
me	

Decoding skills taught to date: *m, s, c, t,* short *a;* consonant *n;* consonant *f;* consonant *p;* short *i;* consonant *b;* consonant *r;* consonant *h;* consonant *g;* short *o;* consonant *d;* consonant *w;* consonant *l;* consonant *x;* short *e;* consonant *y;* consonant *k;* consonant *v;* short *u;* /kw/ spelled *qu;* consonant *j;* consonant *z;* /z/ spelled *s;* consonants *-ck;* /l/ spelled *-ll;* /f/ spelled *-ff;* /s/ spelled *-ss;* /t/ spelled *-ed;* /d/ spelled *-ed;* verb ending *-ing*

Jack the Duck

DECODABLE WORDS

Target Skill: consonants -ck

dock   Jack   Rick
duck   quack   sick

Previously Taught Skills

can   tug
sat

SKILLS APPLIED IN WORDS IN STORY: *m, s, c, t,* short *a*; consonant *n*; short *i*; consonant *r*; consonant *g*; short *o*; consonant *d*; short *u*; /kw/ spelled *qu*; consonant *j*; /z/ spelled *s*

HIGH–FREQUENCY WORDS

a   I   on   the
are   is   said   you

Jack the Duck

His labs can get big logs.

His labs have bags and cans.
Bags and cans go in bins.

Dogs Do Jobs

Dad has two dogs.

His dogs are labs.

His labs can do jobs.

1

His labs have two dog beds.

His labs nap, nap, nap.

4

HIGH-FREQUENCY WORDS TAUGHT TO DATE

Grade 1

a	my
all	never
and	not
animal	of
are	on
away	once
bird	one
call	paper
cold	pull
do	said
does	see
eat	shall
every	the
fall	they
find	three
first	to
five	too
flower	two
for	upon
four	we
full	what
go	where
have	who
he	why
here	you
I	
in	
is	
jump	
live	
look	
me	

Decoding skills taught to date: *m, s, c, t,* short *a;* consonant *n;* consonant *f;* consonant *p;* short *i;* consonant *b;* consonant *r;* consonant *h;* consonant *g;* short *o;* consonant *d;* consonant *w;* consonant *l;* consonant *x;* short *e;* consonant *y;* consonant *k;* consonant *v;* short *u;* /kw/ spelled *qu;* consonant *j;* consonant *z;* /z/ spelled *s;* consonants *-ck;* /l/ spelled *-ll;* /f/ spelled *-ff;* /s/ spelled *-ss;* /t/ spelled *-ed;* /d/ spelled *-ed;* verb ending *-ing*

Dogs Do Jobs

DECODABLE WORDS

Target Skill: /z/ spelled s

bags	bins	dogs	his	labs
beds	cans	has	jobs	logs

Previously Taught Skills

big	Dad	get
can	dog	nap

SKILLS APPLIED IN WORDS IN STORY: *m, s, c, t,* short *a;* consonant *n;* consonant *p;* short *i;* consonant *b;* consonant *h;* consonant *g;* short *o;* consonant *d;* consonant *l;* short *e;* consonant *j*

HIGH–FREQUENCY WORDS

and	do	have	two
are	go	in	

HOUGHTON MIFFLIN   BOSTON

Dogs Do Jobs

I zip my bag. Zip!

I zip my top. Zip!

Zip, Zip, Zip

I zip my kit. Zip!

1

Zip! Zip! Zip!

4

HIGH-FREQUENCY WORDS TAUGHT TO DATE

Grade 1

a	one
and	pull
animal	said
are	see
away	the
bird	they
cold	three
do	to
does	too
fall	two
find	upon
five	we
flower	what
for	where
four	who
full	you
go	
have	
he	
here	
I	
in	
is	
jump	
live	
look	
me	
my	
not	
of	
on	
once	

Decoding skills taught to date: *m, s, c, t,* short *a;* consonant *n;* consonant *f;* consonant *p;* short *i;* consonant *b;* consonant *r;* consonant *h;* consonant *g;* short *o;* consonant *d;* consonant *w;* consonant *l;* consonant *x;* short *e;* consonant *y;* consonant *k;* consonant *v;* short *u;* /kw/ spelled *qu;* consonant *j;* consonant *z;* /z/ spelled *s;* consonants *-ck;* /l/ spelled *-ll;* /f/ spelled *-ff;* /s/ spelled *-ss*

Zip, Zip, Zip

DECODABLE WORDS

Target Skill: consonant z

zip

Previously Taught Skills

bag   top

kit

SKILLS APPLIED IN WORDS IN STORY: *m, s, c, t,* short *a*; consonant *p*; short *i*; consonant *b*; consonant *g*; short *o*; consonant *k*

HIGH–FREQUENCY WORDS

I

my

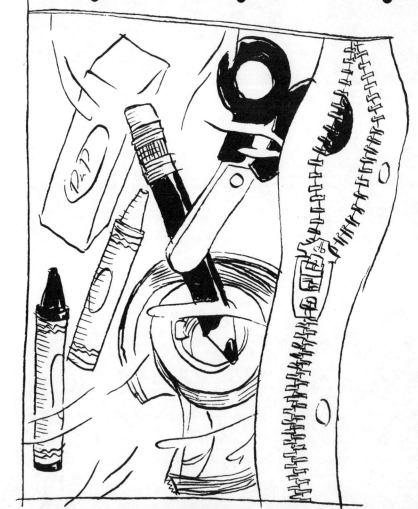

HOUGHTON MIFFLIN   BOSTON

Zip, Zip, Zip

Jan has a hot job.

2

Jed has a box job.

3

A Big Job

Jon has a wet job.

Jen has a jet job.

4

1

HIGH-FREQUENCY WORDS TAUGHT TO DATE

Grade 1

a	one
and	pull
animal	said
are	see
away	the
bird	they
cold	three
do	to
does	too
fall	two
find	upon
five	we
flower	what
for	where
four	who
full	you
go	
have	
he	
here	
I	
in	
is	
jump	
live	
look	
me	
my	
not	
of	
on	
once	

Decoding skills taught to date: m, s, c, t, short a; consonant n; consonant f; consonant p; short i; consonant b; consonant r; consonant h; consonant g; short o; consonant d; consonant w; consonant l; consonant x; short e; consonant y; consonant k; consonant v; short u; /kw/ spelled qu; consonant j; consonant z; /z/ spelled s; consonants -ck; /l/ spelled -ll; /f/ spelled -ff; /s/ spelled -ss

A Big Job

DECODABLE WORDS

Target Skill: consonant *j*

Jan	Jen	job
Jed	jet	Jon

Previously Taught Skills

big	has	wet
box	hot	

SKILLS APPLIED IN WORDS IN STORY: *m, s, c, t,* short *a;* consonant *n;* short *i;* consonant *b;* consonant *h;* consonant *g;* short *o;* consonant *d;* consonant *w;* consonant *x;* short *e;* /z/ spelled *s*

HIGH–FREQUENCY WORDS

a

HOUGHTON MIFFLIN   BOSTON

A Big Job

Quin did not get a hit,
but Quin did not quit.

Quin ran, ran, ran.
Quin got hot, hot, hot.
Will Quin quit?

Did Quin Quit?

Quin did not win,
but Quin did not quit.

Quin did not quit!
Quin is quick, quick, quick!

HIGH-FREQUENCY WORDS TAUGHT TO DATE

Grade 1

a	one
and	pull
animal	said
are	see
away	the
bird	they
cold	three
do	to
does	too
fall	two
find	upon
five	we
flower	what
for	where
four	who
full	you
go	
have	
he	
here	
I	
in	
is	
jump	
live	
look	
me	
my	
not	
of	
on	
once	

Decoding skills taught to date: m, s, c, t, short a; consonant n; consonant f; consonant p; short i; consonant b; consonant r; consonant h; consonant g; short o; consonant d; consonant w; consonant l; consonant x; short e; consonant y; consonant k; consonant v; short u; /kw/ spelled qu; consonant j; consonant z; /z/ spelled s; consonants -ck; /l/ spelled -ll; /f/ spelled -ff; /s/ spelled -ss

DECODABLE WORDS

Target Skill: /kw/ spelled *qu*

quick   quit
Quin

Previously Taught Skills

but	get	hit	ran	will
did	got	hot	Tim	win

SKILLS APPLIED IN WORDS IN STORY: *m, s, c, t,* short *a*; consonant *n*; short *i*; consonant *b*; consonant *r*; consonant *h*; consonant *g*; short *o*; consonant *d*; consonant *w*; short *e*; short *u*; /z/ spelled *s*; consonants *-ck*; /l/ spelled *-ll*

HIGH–FREQUENCY WORDS

a
is
not

HOUGHTON MIFFLIN   BOSTON

Did Quin Quit?

Pup and Cub tug.
Tug! Tug! Tug!

Pup and Cub hug.
Hug! Hug! Hug!

Pup and Cub have fun.
Fun! Fun! Fun!

4

Pup and Cub
Have Fun

Pup and Cub run.
Run! Run! Run!

1

HIGH-FREQUENCY WORDS TAUGHT TO DATE

Grade 1

a	one
and	pull
animal	said
are	see
away	the
bird	they
cold	three
do	to
does	too
fall	two
find	upon
five	we
flower	what
for	where
four	who
full	you
go	
have	
he	
here	
I	
in	
is	
jump	
live	
look	
me	
my	
not	
of	
on	
once	

Decoding skills taught to date: m, s, c, t, short a; consonant n; consonant f; consonant p; short i; consonant b; consonant r; consonant h; consonant g; short o; consonant d; consonant w; consonant l; consonant x; short e; consonant y; consonant k; consonant v; short u; /kw/ spelled qu; consonant j; consonant z; /z/ spelled s; consonants -ck; /l/ spelled -ll; /f/ spelled -ff; /s/ spelled -ss

Pup and Cub Have Fun

DECODABLE WORDS

Target Skill: short *u*

Cub	hug	run
fun	Pup	tug

Previously Taught Skills

(Words listed under *Target Skill* also include previously taught skills.)

SKILLS APPLIED IN WORDS IN STORY: *m, s, c, t,* short *a;* consonant *n;* consonant *f;* consonant *p;* consonant *b;* consonant *r;* consonant *h;* consonant *g*

HIGH–FREQUENCY WORDS

and

have

HOUGHTON MIFFLIN   BOSTON

Pup and Cub Have Fun

I ♥ READING BOOKS

THEME 3
Let's Look Around!

REVIEW BOOK 19   Pup and Cub Have Fun
REVIEW BOOK 20   Did Quin Quit?
REVIEW BOOK 21   A Big Job
REVIEW BOOK 22   Zip, Zip, Zip
REVIEW BOOK 23   Dogs Do Jobs
REVIEW BOOK 24   Jack the Duck

REVIEW BOOK 25   Bill and Jill
REVIEW BOOK 26   Muff in a Puff!
REVIEW BOOK 27   Tess and Bess
REVIEW BOOK 28   Mac Missed
REVIEW BOOK 29   Ron Filled
REVIEW BOOK 30   Cat Is Missing!

Val, Val, Val,
get in the van!

Val, Val, Val,
do not get wet!

2

3

Val, Val, Val,
go to the vet.

4

Val, Val, Val

Val, Val, Val,
run to the pan.

1

HIGH-FREQUENCY WORDS TAUGHT TO DATE

Grade 1

a	two
and	upon
are	we
away	what
do	where
does	who
find	you
five	
for	
four	
go	
have	
he	
here	
I	
in	
is	
jump	
live	
me	
my	
not	
on	
once	
one	
pull	
said	
the	
they	
three	
to	
too	

Decoding skills taught to date: *m, s, c, t,* short *a;* consonant *n;* consonant *f;* consonant *p;* short *i;* consonant *b;* consonant *r;* consonant *h;* consonant *g;* short *o;* consonant *d;* consonant *w;* consonant *l;* consonant *x;* short *e;* consonant *y;* consonant *k;* consonant *v;* short *u;* /kw/ spelled *qu;* consonant *j;* consonant *z*

Val, Val, Val

DECODABLE WORDS

Target Skill: consonant v

Val   vet
van

Previously Taught Skills

get   run
pan   wet

SKILLS APPLIED IN WORDS IN STORY: *m, s, c, t,* short *a;* consonant *n;* consonant *p;* short *i;* consonant *r;* consonant *g;* short *o;* consonant *w;* consonant *l;* short *e;* short *u*

HIGH–FREQUENCY WORDS

do   not
go   the
in   to

HOUGHTON MIFFLIN   BOSTON

Val, Val, Val

"Kid! Kid!" said Ken.
"Do not nip at Yak!"

"Kid! Kid!" said Ken.
"Do not nip my leg!"

Ken fed the kid.

The kid did not nip Yak.

The kid did not nip Ken.

Kid, Kid!

Kid

Here is Ken.

Here is a kid.

HIGH-FREQUENCY WORDS TAUGHT TO DATE

Grade 1

a
and
are
away
do
does
find
five
for
four
go
have
he
here
I
in
is
jump
live
me
my
not
on
once
one
pull
said
the
they
three
to
too

two
upon
we
what
where
who
you

Decoding skills taught to date: m, s, c, t, short a; consonant n; consonant f; consonant p; short i; consonant b; consonant r; consonant h; consonant g; short o; consonant d; consonant w; consonant l; consonant x; short e; consonant y; consonant k; consonant v; short u; /kw/ spelled qu; consonant j; consonant z

Kid, Kid!

DECODABLE WORDS

Target Skill: consonant _k_

Ken	Yak
kid	

Previously Taught Skills

at	fed	nip
did	leg	

SKILLS APPLIED IN WORDS IN STORY: _m, s, c, t,_ short _a_; consonant _n_; consonant _f_; consonant _p_; short _i_; consonant _g_; short _o_; consonant _d_; consonant _l_; short _e_; consonant _y_

HIGH–FREQUENCY WORDS

a	is	said
do	my	the
here	not	

Kid, Kid!

Kid

"Yan, can you run yet?"
said Kim.
"Not yet," said Yan.

"Yan, can you tag yet?"
said Kim.
"Yes, I can," said Yan.

Not Yet

"Yan, can you hit yet?"
said Kim.
"Not yet," said Yan.

Yes! Yes! Yes!

HIGH-FREQUENCY WORDS TAUGHT TO DATE

Grade 1

a	two
and	upon
are	we
away	what
do	where
does	who
find	you
five	
for	
four	
go	
have	
he	
here	
I	
in	
is	
jump	
live	
me	
my	
not	
on	
once	
one	
pull	
said	
the	
they	
three	
to	
too	

Decoding skills taught to date: *m, s, c, t,* short *a;* consonant *n;* consonant *f;* consonant *p;* short *i;* consonant *b;* consonant *r;* consonant *h;* consonant *g;* short *o;* consonant *d;* consonant *w;* consonant *l;* consonant *x;* short *e;* consonant *y;* consonant *k;* consonant *v;* short *u;* /kw/ spelled *qu;* consonant *j;* consonant *z*

Not Yet

HOUGHTON MIFFLIN   BOSTON

Not Yet

Meg met a yak.

You can not pet it, Meg.

A hen! A hen!

You can not get in the

hen pen, Meg.

Meg

What can Meg do?

Meg **can** get the pig wet!

Here is a fox den.

Let the fox get a nap, Meg.

HIGH-FREQUENCY WORDS TAUGHT TO DATE

Grade 1

a
and
are
away
do
does
find
five
for
four
go
have
he
here
I
in
is
jump
live
me
my
not
on
once
one
pull
said
the
they
three
to

too
two
upon
we
what
where
who
you

Decoding skills taught to date: m, s, c, t, short a; consonant n; consonant f; consonant p; short i; consonant b; consonant r; consonant h; consonant g; short o; consonant d; consonant w; consonant l; consonant x; short e; consonant y; consonant k; consonant v; short u; /kw/ spelled qu; consonant j; consonant z

Meg

DECODABLE WORDS

Target Skill: short *e*

den	hen	Meg	pen	wet
get	let	met	pet	

Previously Taught Skills

can	it	pig
fox	nap	yak

SKILLS APPLIED IN WORDS IN STORY: *m, s, c, t,* short *a*; consonant *n*; consonant *f*; consonant *p*; short *i*; consonant *h*; consonant *g*; short *o*; consonant *d*; consonant *w*; consonant *l*; consonant *x*; consonant *y*; consonant *k*

HIGH–FREQUENCY WORDS

a	in	the
do	is	what
here	not	you

HOUGHTON MIFFLIN   BOSTON

Meg

It is wax.

Here is a box.

BOOK 14

It is a fox.

Fox, fox, fox!

Max Is Six

Max is six.

Six, six, six!

HIGH-FREQUENCY WORDS TAUGHT TO DATE

Grade 1

a
and
do
find
five
for
four
go
have
here
I
in
is
jump
me
my
not
on
once
one
said
the
three
to
too
two
upon
we
what
who
you

Decoding skills taught to date: *m, s, c, t,* short *a;* consonant *n;* consonant *f;* consonant *p;* short *i;* consonant *b;* consonant *r;* consonant *h;* consonant *g;* short *o;* consonant *d;* consonant *w;* consonant *l;* consonant *x;* short *e;* consonant *y;* consonant *k;* consonant *v*

Max Is Six

DECODABLE WORDS

Target Skill: consonant _x_

box   Max   wax
fox   six

Previously Taught Skills

it

SKILLS APPLIED IN WORDS IN STORY: _m, s, c, t_, short _a_; consonant _f_; short _i_;
consonant _b_; short _o_; consonant _w_

HIGH–FREQUENCY WORDS

a
here
<u>is</u>

Underscored high-frequency words are introduced in this week's instruction.

Max Is Six

HOUGHTON MIFFLIN   BOSTON

Is his leg bad?

"Sit in my lap, Len," said Mom.

"Let me fix it."

2

3

Len

Len hit his leg on a log.

"Have a sip, Len," said Mom.
Len had a lot!

HIGH-FREQUENCY WORDS TAUGHT TO DATE

Grade 1

a
and
do
find
five
for
four
go
have
here
I
in
is
jump
me
my
not
on
once
one
said
the
three
to
too
two
upon
we
what
who
you

Decoding skills taught to date: *m, s, c, t,* short *a;* consonant *n;* consonant *f;* consonant *p;* short *i;* consonant *b;* consonant *r;* consonant *h;* consonant *g;* short *o;* consonant *d;* consonant *w;* consonant *l;* consonant *x;* short *e;* consonant *y;* consonant *k;* consonant *v*

Len

DECODABLE WORDS

Target Skill: consonant l

lap	Len	log
leg	let	lot

Previously Taught Skills

bad	had	hit	Mom	sit
fix	his	it	sip	

SKILLS APPLIED IN WORDS IN STORY: *m, s, c, t*, short *a*; consonant *n*; consonant *f*; consonant *p*; short *i*; consonant *b*; consonant *h*; consonant *g*; short *o*; consonant *d*; consonant *x*; short *e*

HIGH-FREQUENCY WORDS

a	in	me	on
have	is	my	said

Underscored high-frequency words are introduced in this week's instruction.

HOUGHTON MIFFLIN   BOSTON

Len

Can we fix his wig?

We pin the wig.

Pin! Pin! Pin!

We wax the wig.

Wax! Wax! Wax!

Wa! Wa! Wa!

Wag Pig is sad.

Wag Pig hid the wig.

Wag Pig got a big hat.

Wag Pig can go to the Pig Hop!

4

Wag Pig and the Wig

Wag Pig has a wig.

It is a bad wig.

Wag Pig can not go to the Pig Hop.

1

HIGH-FREQUENCY WORDS TAUGHT TO DATE

Grade 1

a
and
do
find
five
for
four
go
have
here
I
in
is
jump
me
my
not
on
once
one
said
the
three
to
too
two
upon
we
what
who
you

Decoding skills taught to date: m, s, c, t, short a; consonant n; consonant f; consonant p; short i; consonant b; consonant r; consonant h; consonant g; short o; consonant d; consonant w; consonant l; consonant x; short e; consonant y; consonant k; consonant v

Wag Pig and the Wig

DECODABLE WORDS

Target Skill: consonant w

wa	wax
Wag	wig

Previously Taught Skills

bad	fix	hat	Hop	pin
big	got	hid	it	sad
can	has	his	Pig	

SKILLS APPLIED IN WORDS IN STORY: *m, s, c, t,* short *a*; consonant *n*; consonant *f*; consonant *p*; short *i*; consonant *b*; consonant *h*; consonant *g*; short *o*; consonant *d*; consonant *x*

HIGH–FREQUENCY WORDS

a	<u>is</u>	to
and	not	we
go	the	

Underscored high-frequency words are introduced in this week's instruction.

HOUGHTON MIFFLIN   BOSTON

Wag Pig and the Wig

Dot is not here!
Dan is sad.

Can Dan find Dot?
"Dot! Dot! Dot!"

Here is Dot in a lid!

Dan is not sad.

4

Dot Hid

Here is Dot.

Dot hid in a lid.

1

HIGH-FREQUENCY WORDS TAUGHT TO DATE

Grade 1

a
and
do
find
five
for
four
go
have
here
I
in
is
jump
me
my
not
on
once
one
said
the
three
to
too
two
upon
we
what
who
you

Decoding skills taught to date: m, s, c, t, short *a*; consonant *n*; consonant *f*; consonant *p*; short *i*; consonant *b*; consonant *r*; consonant *h*; consonant *g*; short *o*; consonant *d*; consonant *w*; consonant *l*; consonant *x*; short *e*; consonant *y*; consonant *k*; consonant *v*

Dot Hid

Target Skill: consonant d

Dan	hid	sad
Dot	lid	

Previously Taught Skills

can

SKILLS APPLIED IN WORDS IN STORY: *m, s, c, t,* short *a;* consonant *n;* short *i;* consonant *h;* short *o;* consonant *l*

HIGH-FREQUENCY WORDS

a	here	is
find	in	not

Underscored high-frequency words are introduced in this week's instruction.

HOUGHTON MIFFLIN BOSTON

Dot Hid

Dot and Dom hop on a box.
Hop! Hop! Hop!

2

Dot and Dom hop on a log.
Hop! Hop! Hop!

3

Dot and Dom do **not** hop a lot.

Dot and Dom Hop

Dot and Dom hop a lot.
Hop! Hop! Hop!

HIGH-FREQUENCY WORDS TAUGHT TO DATE

Grade 1

a
and
do
find
five
for
four
go
have
here
I
in
is
jump
me
my
not
on
once
one
said
the
three
to
too
two
upon
we
what
who
you

Decoding skills taught to date: m, s, c, t, short a; consonant n; consonant f; consonant p; short i; consonant b; consonant r; consonant h; consonant g; short o; consonant d; consonant w; consonant l; consonant x; short e; consonant y; consonant k; consonant v

Dot and Dom Hop

DECODABLE WORDS

Target Skill: short *o*

box	Dot	log
Dom	hop	lot

Previously Taught Skills

(Words listed under *Target Skill* also include previously taught skills.)

SKILLS APPLIED IN WORDS IN STORY: *m, s, c, t,* short *a*; consonant *n*; consonant *p*; consonant *b*; consonant *h*; consonant *g*; consonant *d*; consonant *l*; consonant *x*

HIGH–FREQUENCY WORDS

a	<u>do</u>	on
and	not	

Underscored high-frequency words are introduced in this week's instruction.

HOUGHTON MIFFLIN   BOSTON

short *o*

REVIEW BOOK 10

Dot and Dom Hop

Tim, go tag Mag.

Tag!

Mag, go tag Tim.

Tag!

Tag!

Tag! Tag!

Mag and Tim can tag.

4

1

HIGH-FREQUENCY WORDS TAUGHT TO DATE

Grade 1

a
and
find
five
four
go
have
here
in
jump
not
on
once
one
the
three
to
too
two
upon
we
what
who

Decoding skills taught to date: *m, s, c, t,* short *a;* consonant *n;* consonant *f;* consonant *p;* short *i;* consonant *b;* consonant *r;* consonant *h;* consonant *g;* short *o;* consonant *d;* consonant *w;* consonant *l;* consonant *x*

Tag!

DECODABLE WORDS

Target Skill: consonant _g_

Mag

tag

Previously Taught Skills

can

Tim

SKILLS APPLIED IN WORDS IN STORY: _m, s, c, t,_ short _a;_ consonant _n;_ short _i_

HIGH–FREQUENCY WORDS

and

go

HOUGHTON MIFFLIN   BOSTON

Tag!

Here is his hat.
His hat is not on him.

Hap can jump.
Jump, Hap!

2

3

Hap has his hat!
His hat is on him.

4

Hap Has a Hat

Here is Hap.

1

HIGH-FREQUENCY WORDS TAUGHT TO DATE

Grade 1

a
and
find
five
four
go
have
here
in
jump
not
on
once
one
the
three
to
too
two
upon
we
what
who

Decoding skills taught to date: m, s, c, t, short a; consonant n; consonant f; consonant p; short i; consonant b; consonant r; consonant h; consonant g; short o; consonant d; consonant w; consonant l; consonant x

Hap Has a Hat

DECODABLE WORDS

Target Skill: consonant _h_

Hap	hat	his
has	him	

Previously Taught Skills

can

is

SKILLS APPLIED IN WORDS IN STORY: _m, s, c, t,_ short _a_; consonant _n_; consonant _p_; short _i_; short _o_

HIGH–FREQUENCY WORDS

a	not
here	on
jump	

HOUGHTON MIFFLIN   BOSTON

Hap Has a Hat

The rod is bad.

Rox got the rod.

Rox got a rag.

Can Rox Fix It?

The rig can not go.
Can Rox fix it?

1

The man ran the rig. **Rrrrr!**
The rig can go. Rox did fix it!

4

HIGH-FREQUENCY WORDS TAUGHT TO DATE

Grade 1

a
and
find
five
four
go
have
here
in
jump
not
on
once
one
the
three
to
too
two
upon
we
what
who

Decoding skills taught to date: *m, s, c, t,* short *a;* consonant *n;* consonant *f;* consonant *p;* short *i;* consonant *b;* consonant *r;* consonant *h;* consonant *g;* short *o;* consonant *d;* consonant *w;* consonant *l;* consonant *x*

Can Rox Fix It?

DECODABLE WORDS

Target Skill: consonant *r*

rag	rig	Rox
ran	rod	Rrrrr

Previously Taught Skills

bad	did	got	it
can	fix	is	man

SKILLS APPLIED IN WORDS IN STORY: *m, s, c, t,* short *a*; consonant *n*; consonant *f*; short *i*; consonant *b*; consonant *g*; short *o*; consonant *d*; consonant *x*

HIGH–FREQUENCY WORDS

a	not
go	the

HOUGHTON MIFFLIN   BOSTON

Can a big bat fit?

A big bat can fit in the big bin!

Can a big box fit?

A big box can fit in the big bin!

Can the big lid fit on the big bin?
The big lid **can** fit on the big bin!

A Big Bin

Can a bib fit in the big bin?
A bib can fit in the big bin.

HIGH-FREQUENCY WORDS TAUGHT TO DATE

Grade 1

a
and
find
five
four
go
have
here
in
jump
not
on
once
one
the
three
to
too
two
upon
we
what
who

Decoding skills taught to date: m, s, c, t, short a; consonant n; consonant f; consonant p; short i; consonant b; consonant r; consonant h; consonant g; short o; consonant d; consonant w; consonant l; consonant x

A Big Bin

DECODABLE WORDS

Target Skill: consonant *b*

bat	big	box
bib	bin	

Previously Taught Skills

can	lid
fit	

SKILLS APPLIED IN WORDS IN STORY: *m, s, c, t,* short *a;* consonant *n;* consonant *f;* short *i;* consonant *g;* short *o;* consonant *d;* consonant *l;* consonant *x*

HIGH–FREQUENCY WORDS

a	on
<u>in</u>	the

Underscored high-frequency words are introduced in this week's instruction.

HOUGHTON MIFFLIN   BOSTON

A Big Bin

It is a pig.

The pig is not big.

Tim and Mim sit and sip.

A Big Pig Bib

Tim and Mim find a bib.

A big pig bib!

It is Tim.

It is Mim.

4

1

Grade 1

a
and
find
five
four
go
have
here
in
jump
not
on
once
one
the
three
to
too
two
upon
we
what
who

Decoding skills taught to date: *m, s, c, t,* short *a;* consonant *n;* consonant *f;* consonant *p;* short *i;* consonant *b;* consonant *r;* consonant *h;* consonant *g;* short *o;* consonant *d;* consonant *w;* consonant *l;* consonant *x*

A Big Pig Bib

DECODABLE WORDS

Target Skill: short *i*

bib	is	Mim	sip	Tim
big	it	pig	sit	

Previously Taught Skills

(Words listed under *Target Skill* also include previously taught skills.)

SKILLS APPLIED IN WORDS IN STORY: *m, s, c, t,* short *a*; consonant *n*; consonant *p*; consonant *b*; consonant *g*; short *o*

HIGH–FREQUENCY WORDS

a	not
and	the
find	

HOUGHTON MIFFLIN   BOSTON

A Big Pig Bib

I ♥ LOVE READING BOOKS

THEME 2
Surprise!

REVIEW BOOK	5	A Big Pig Bib
REVIEW BOOK	6	A Big Bin
REVIEW BOOK	7	Can Rox Fix It?
REVIEW BOOK	8	Hap Has a Hat
REVIEW BOOK	9	Tag!
REVIEW BOOK	10	Dot and Dom Hop
REVIEW BOOK	11	Dot Hid

REVIEW BOOK	12	Wag Pig and the Wig
REVIEW BOOK	13	Len
REVIEW BOOK	14	Max Is Six
REVIEW BOOK	15	Meg
REVIEW BOOK	16	Not Yet
REVIEW BOOK	17	Kid, Kid!
REVIEW BOOK	18	Val, Val, Val

Tap, tap, tap.
Pat can not nap.

2

Tap, tap, tap.
Sap on the cap.

3

Can Pat nap?

Not here, Pat!

Can Pat Nap?

Pat can nap.

HIGH-FREQUENCY WORDS TAUGHT TO DATE

Grade 1

a
and
find
go
have
here
jump
not
on
one
the
to
too
we
who

Decoding skills taught to date: m, s, c, t, short a; consonant n; consonant f; consonant p; short i; consonant b; consonant r; consonant h; consonant g

Can Pat Nap?

DECODABLE WORDS

Target Skill: consonant *p*

cap	Pat	tap
nap	sap	

Previously Taught Skills

can

SKILLS APPLIED IN WORDS IN STORY: *m, s, c, t,* short *a*; consonant *n*

HIGH–FREQUENCY WORDS

here	the
not	
on	

HOUGHTON MIFFLIN   BOSTON

Can Pat Nap?

Find a fat, fat, fat cat!

2

Fat, fat, fat, fat!
Too fat!

3

Fat, Fat Cat

Not a fat cat.

Fat, fat cat.

HIGH-FREQUENCY WORDS TAUGHT TO DATE

Grade 1

a
and
find
go
have
here
jump
not
on
one
the
to
too
we
who

Decoding skills taught to date: *m, s, c, t,* short *a;* consonant *n;* consonant *f;* consonant *p;* short *i;* consonant *b;* consonant *r;* consonant *h;* consonant *g*

Fat, Fat Cat

DECODABLE WORDS

Target Skill: consonant f

fat

Previously Taught Skills

cat

SKILLS APPLIED IN WORDS IN STORY: *m, s, c, t,* short *a*

HIGH-FREQUENCY WORDS

<u>a</u>   not

<u>find</u>   too

Underscored high-frequency words are introduced in this week's instruction.

HOUGHTON MIFFLIN   BOSTON

Fat, Fat Cat

Nat and Nan have a tin can.

Nat and Nan pat Cat.

Cat can nap, nap, nap.

Nan, Nat, and Cat

Nan   Nat   Cat

Grade 1

a
and
find
go
have
here
jump
not
on
one
the
to
too
we
who

Decoding skills taught to date: m, s, c, t, short a; consonant n; consonant f; consonant p; short i; consonant b; consonant r; consonant h; consonant g

Nan, Nat, and Cat

DECODABLE WORDS

Target Skill: consonant *n*

can	nap	tin
Nan	Nat	

Previously Taught Skills

Cat

pat

SKILLS APPLIED IN WORDS IN STORY: *m, s, c, t,* short *a;* consonant *p;* short *i*

HIGH-FREQUENCY WORDS

<u>a</u>	<u>have</u>
and	

Underscored high-frequency words are introduced in this week's instruction.

HOUGHTON MIFFLIN   BOSTON

Nan, Nat, and Cat

Cam sat. Tam sat. Mac sat.

Cat! Cat! Cat!

Cat sat on the mat.

Cat! Cat! Cat!

Mat!

HIGH-FREQUENCY WORDS TAUGHT TO DATE

Grade 1

and
go
here
jump
not
on
the
too
we

Decoding skills taught to date: m, s, c, t, short a; consonant n; consonant f; consonant p

Cat! Cat! Cat!

DECODABLE WORDS

Target Skill: *m, s, c, t,* **short** *a*

Cam	Mac	sat
Cat	mat	Tam

Previously Taught Skills

(Words listed under *Target Skill* also include previously taught skills.)

SKILLS APPLIED IN WORDS IN STORY: *m, s, c, t,* short *a*

HIGH–FREQUENCY WORDS

on

the

HOUGHTON MIFFLIN   BOSTON

Cat! Cat! Cat!

I LOVE READING BOOKS

THEME 1
All Together Now

REVIEW BOOK 1   Cat! Cat! Cat!
REVIEW BOOK 2   Nan, Nat, and Cat
REVIEW BOOK 3   Fat, Fat Cat
REVIEW BOOK 4   Can Pat Nap?